Oct 75

The Marriage of Figaro

(Le Nozze di Figaro.)

Piano-vocal score. English & Italian,

Comic Opera in four Acts by

Wolfgang Amadeus Mozart

Words by Lorenzo da Ponte

after Beaumarchais' "La Folle Journée
ou Le Marriage de Figaro"

English Version by Edward J. Dent

Vocal Score by Erwin Stein

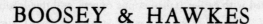

BOOSEY & HAWKES

PRINTED IN U. S. A.

THE comedy of Beaumarchais from which the plot of Mozart's opera is taken was a sequel to an earlier play by the same author, *Le Barbier de Séville*, set to music by Rossini in 1816. *The Barber of Seville* is a harmless comedy in the old Italian manner, dealing with the intrigues by which Count Almaviva, assisted by the barber Figaro, secured the hand of the rich heiress Rosina despite the opposition of her guardian Doctor Bartolo. In *The Marriage of Figaro* we find the Count tired of his wife and making love to her maid Susanna, who is engaged to be married to Figaro, now the Count's valet. In this he is abetted by Basilio, the priest-music-master of the earlier play, and by Marcellina, Doctor Bartolo's elderly housekeeper, who has lent money to Figaro on condition that if he cannot repay her, he shall marry her Susanna virtuously resists the Count's temptations, although quite willing to make Figaro jealous, and Figaro is discovered to be the natural son of Doctor Bartolo and Marcellina. The complicated misadventures of the play are due mainly to the page Cherubino, who is always being found in the wrong place. The comedy ends with the discomfiture of the Count and his reconciliation with his wife.

The original play has often been called " the prologue to the French Revolution," for it is a biting satire on the privileges of the nobility, and Figaro, claiming the rights of the old Italian Harlequin to talk to the audience and express his views on everything, is made the mouthpiece of the author's subversive political opinions. For several years the play was forbidden to be acted in Paris, and at the time when Mozart set it to music, its performance was still forbidden in Vienna. But what was forbidden as a play managed to pass the censorship as an Italian opera. Figaro's dangerous observations were eliminated, but we may be fairly sure that the Viennese audience knew perfectly well what was left out, as the French play was accessible to all who could buy and read it. There can be no doubt that the political sympathies of both Da Ponte and Mozart were with the ideas that found vent in Paris in 1789 and that they deliberately chose this unusual subject for their opera with a view to popular success. It may be pointed out here that their two subsequent operas, *Don Giovanni* and *Così fan Tutte* both make fun of the privileged classes and present them in ridiculous situations, while Mozart's last opera, *The Magic Flute*, written to German words for a humbler type of audience, bids a definite farewell to the ideas of the eighteenth century and opens the door to the doctrines of Liberty, Equality and Fraternity.

The Marriage of Figaro is remarkable for the amount of action that takes place on the stage, as compared with earlier Italian comic operas, and this liveliness of movement is doubtless one of the qualities which has made Mozart's work eternally popular. The original play is in five acts, whereas Italian comic operas were almost invariably in three, or sometimes even two ; Mozart's opera is in four acts, an arrangement necessitated no doubt by the impossibility of compressing Beaumarchais' complicated plot into a smaller number. The only previous case of an Italian comic opera in four acts is in fact Paisiello's adaptation of Beaumarchais' *Barbier de Séville* (1782).

E.J.D.

Characters

(in the order of their appearance)

Sung by

Figaro, *servant to Count Almaviva*	Bass	Cesare Siepi
Susanna, *maid to Countess Almaviva*	Soprano	Hilde Gueden
Doctor Bartolo	Bass	Fernando Corena
Marcellina, *his housekeeper*	Soprano	Hilde Roessel-Majdan
Cherubino, *page to the Countess*	Soprano	Suzanne Danco
Count Almaviva	Baritone	Alfred Poell
Don Basilio, *organist and music-master*	Tenor	Murray Dickie
Countess Almaviva	Soprano	Lisa della Casa
Antonio, *a gardener, uncle to Susanna*	Bass	Harald Pröglhöf
Don Curzio, *a lawyer*	Tenor	Hugo Meyer-Welfing
Barbarina, *daughter of Antonio*	Soprano	Anny Felbermayer

Chorus of Villagers

The action covers one day and takes place in the Castle and grounds of Aguas Frescas, the domain of Count Almaviva near Seville.

with the

VIENNA STATE OPERA CHORUS

Director: Dr. Richard Rossmayer

and the

VIENNA PHILHARMONIC ORCHESTRA

Conductor: ERICH KLEIBER

Index

Act III

In addition to the grace-notes which Mozart himself wrote down in the vocal parts it has been customary to sing many additional appoggiaturas, especially in recitatives, following the Italian convention which dates back to long before the days of Mozart. These appoggiaturas have not been printed in the present score because they have always been traditionally left to the discretion of the singers. No hard and fast rule can be laid down for their performance, but in most cases where a descending phrase has a feminine ending, i.e., with an accented penultimate syllable followed by a final syllable on a weak beat, both being given the same musical note, the strong beat should be treated as an appoggiatura and sung to the note one degree above that actually written, so that the cadence falls by a tone or semitone to the final note.

Examples :

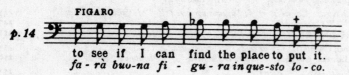

FIGARO

p. 14

to see if I can find the place to put it.
fa - rà buo-na fi - gu- ra in que-sto lo - co.

FIGARO

p. 19

Quick, tell me!
Fa pre-sto!

CHERUBINO

p. 53

And ev'n if none be near me,   No, ne'er a soul to hear me,
E se non ho chi m'o-da,   e se non ho chi m'o-da,

Application for permission to use this English translation in connection with a performance of the Opera should be made to the Oxford University Press, Music Department, 44, Conduit Street, London, W.1

The Marriage of Figaro
Overture

W. A. MOZART

1

The Marriage of Figaro

The Marriage of Figaro

B.& H. 15960

The Marriage of Figaro

The Marriage of Figaro

6

The Marriage of Figaro

The Marriage of Figaro

8

ACT I

A half-furnished room, a large arm-chair in centre. Figaro is measuring the floor; Susanna before a mirror is trying on a hat.

№ 1 Duet

B.& H. 15960

The Marriage of Figaro

11

The Marriage of Figaro

B. & H. 15960

The Marriage of Figaro

Recitative

Susanna

Tell me, what are you do - ing, mea - sur - ing the
Co - sa stai mi - su - ran - do, ca - ro il

room with a yard-stick?

Figaro

I'm think-ing a-bout the bed which his lordship said he'd
mio Fi - ga - ret - to? Io guar - do se quel let - to, che ci de-sti-na il

give us, to see if I can find the place to put it.

Susanna

But, not in
Con - te, fa - rà buo - na fi - gu-ra in que-sto lo - co. In que-sta

Figaro

this room? Sure - ly; this is the room my lord himself has assign'd us.
stan - za? Cer - to, a noi la ce - de ge - ne - ro-so il pa - dro - ne..

Susanna

You may
Io per

Figaro

sleep here a-lone then.

What's your ob-jec - tion?
me te la do - no. E la ra-gi - one?

Susanna

I have rea-son e-nough.
La ra-gio - ne l'ho qui.

Figaro

Then
Per

B. & H. 15960

why won't you say what your rea-son may be? | **Susanna** Why should I tell you?
che non puoi far, che pas-si un pò quì! | Per-chè non vo-glio;

Figaro
aren't you my hum-ble servant? | Yours to com-mand, ma'am; but I can see no
sei tu mio ser-vo, o nò? | Ma non ca-pi-sco per-chè tan-to ti

rea-son for re-fus-ing a room that's so con-ve-nient. | **Susanna** Because
spia-ce la più com-mo-da stan-za del pa-laz-zo. | Perch'io

Figaro
I am Su-san-na, and you're a block-head. Thank you, you're far too
son la Su-san-na, e tu sei paz-zo. Gra-zie, non tan-ti e-

flatt'r-ing. But now tell me, could you find a-ny room to suit us bet-ter?
-lo-gi; guarda un po-co, se po-tria me-glio stare in al-tro lo-co.

The Marriage of Figaro

B. & H. 15960

Nº 2 Duet Susanna and Figaro

The Marriage of Figaro

B.& H. 15960

The Marriage of Figaro

B. & H. 15960

20

The Marriage of Figaro

B. & H. 15960

Recitative

Susanna

Be qui-et, and then I'll tell you.
Or be - ne; a - scol - ta e ta - ci.

Figaro

Well then, what is your
Par - la, che-c'è di

Susanna

se - cret? His no-ble lord-ship finds he is tir'd of hunt-ing all the
nuo - vo? Il si-gnor Con - te, stan-co d'an-dar cac-cian-do le stra-

S. coun-try for a-morous ad-ven-tures; so he means to come home now, in the hope of a
-nie - re bel-lez-ze fo-re-stie - re, vuole an - cor nel ca-stel - lo, ri-ten-tar la sua

S. new one. But it is not the Coun-tess, let me tell you, that his
sor-te. N'è già di sua con - sor-te, ba-da be - ne, ap-pe-

Figaro   **Susanna**

S. lord-ship is af - ter. Who is it this time? No one else but Su-san - na.
-ti - to gli vie-ne. E di chi dun-que? Del-la tua Su-san-net-ta.

Figaro   **Susanna**

S. What, you? The ve - ry same, sir. and you can see now how
Di te? Di me me - des-ma, ed ha spe-ran - za ch'al

Figaro

S. use-ful he will find it if he gives us a room where I'm his neigh-bour. Bra-vo!
no-bil suo pro-get-to u-til - lis-si-ma sia tal vi-ci-nan-za. Bra-vo!

The Marriage of Figaro

B. & H. 15960

S. lord gave me a dow-ry just to reward your ser-vice? I'm sure that I de-
fos-se la mia do-te mer-to del tuo bel mu-so? Me n'e-ra lu-sin-

Figaro

F. -serv'd it. Have you for-got-ten a cer-tain ve-ry old-es-ta-blish'd
ga-to. Ei la de-sti-na per ot-ten-er da me cer-te mezz'

Susanna

S. privilege which the Lord of the Man-or__ Privilege! has not my lord him-self a-
o-re che il di-rit-to feu-da-le__ Co-me! ne feu-di suo-i non l'ha il

Figaro

F. -bo-lish'd it for e-ver? He has, but he re-grets it; and he would
Con-te a-bo-li-to? Eb-ben, o-ra è pen-ti-to, e par che

Susanna

S. like to buy it back a-gain from me. Would he? I like that! That's what I call a
ten-ti ri-scat-tar-lo da me. Bra-vo! mi pia-ce; che ca-ro si-gnor

Figaro

-pre - ciate your most gen - er - ous in - ten - tions.
schiet - to tut-to il vo - - stro pro - get - to.

The king ap - points you am - bas-sa-dor in
A Lon - dra, è ve - ro? voi mi -

Lon - don, I go as cour - ier, and my Su -
-ni - stro, io cor - rie - ro, e la Su -

-san - na, 'con - fi - den - tial at - ta - chée'! No, I'm
-san - na, se - gre - ta am-ba-scia-tri - ce. Non sa -

Andante

hang'd if she does_ Fi - ga - ro knows bet - ter!
-rà, non sa - rà, Fi - ga - ro il di - ce!

№ 3 Cavatina

Allegretto

Figaro: If you are af-ter a lit-tle a-musement, if you are af-ter a little a-musement, You may go danc-ing, but I'll play the tune. You may go danc-ing, but I'll play the tune, yes, I'll play the tune, yes, I'll play the tune. I'll teach your lord-ship steps and de-port-ment, New kinds of ca-pers you shall learn

Se vuol bal-la-re, sig-nor Con-ti-no, se vuol bal-la-re, sig-nor Con-ti-no, il chi-tar-ri-no le suo-ne-rò, il chi-tar-ri-no le suo-ne-rò, si, le suo-ne-rò, si, le suo-ne-rò. Se vuol ve-ni-re nel-la mia sco-la, la ca-pri-o-la le in-se-gne-

The Marriage of Figaro

I'll put a spoke in your wheel if I can, I'll put a spoke in your wheel if I
tut-te le mac-chi-ne ro-ve-scie-rò, tut-te le mac-chi-ne ro-ve-scie-

can, I'll put a spoke in your wheel if I can. If you are af-ter a lit-tle a-
rò, ro-ve-scie-rò, ro-ve-scie-rò. Se vuol bal-la-re, sig-nor Con-

Tempo I

-musement, if you are af-ter a lit-tle a-musement, You may go dancing, but I'll play the
-ti-no, se vuol bal-la-re, sig-nor Con-ti-no, il chi-tar-ri-no le suo-ne-

tune. You may go dancing, but I'll play the tune, yes, I'll play the tune, yes, I'll play the
-rò, il chi-tar-ri-no le suo-ne-rò, si, le suo-ne-rò, si, le suo-ne-

Presto Exit

tune.
-rò.

nter Bartolo and Marcellina

Recitative

Bartolo

Then why in Hea-ven's name did you wait un-til this morn-ing to con-a
Ed a - spet - ta - te il gior - no fis-sa-to per le noz - ze, a par-

Marcellina

-sult me on this mat - ter? I can as - sure you I don't mean to give in yet.
-lar - mi di que - sto? Io non mi per - do, dot-tor mio, di cor-ra - gio,

It takes a ve-ry lit - tle to break off an en-gage-ment, e-ven la - ter than
per romper de'spon-sa - li più a-van-za-ti di que - sto, ba - stò spesso un pre-

this time. I've got my con-tract, and I'll see he ful-fils it; he has
-te - sto; ed e-gli ha me-co, ol-tre que - sto con-trat-to, cer-ti im-

fur-ther ob-li-ga-tions. Now then! Our plan must be to fright-en Su-
-pe-gni_ so i o_ ba - sta! Con-vie-ne la Su-san-na at-ter-

Nº 4 Aria

Allegro con spirito

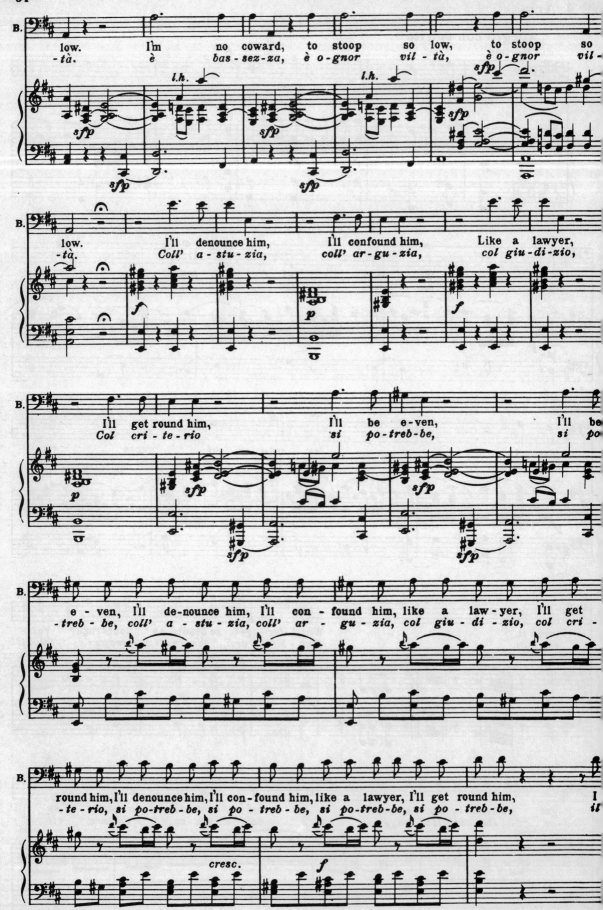

swear I will, ma'am, I swear I will, ma'am, I swear I will, ma'am,
fat - to è se - rio, il fat - to è se - rio, il fat - to è se - rio;

I'm no fool, the man shall know, I'm no fool, the man shall know,
ma cre - de - te si fa - rà, ma cre - de - te si fa - rà.

Once I can seize on the right op - por -
Se tut - to il co - di - ce do - ves - si

- tu - ni - ty, I shall not let him get off with im - pu - ni - ty. I can em - barrass him, wor - ry him,
vol - ge - re, se tut - to l'in - di - ce do - ves - si leg - ge - re, con un e - qui - vo - co, con un si -

harass him; Do as I tell you, and leave it to me, Once I can seize on the right op - por -
- no - ni - mo, qual - che gar - bu - glio si tro - ve - rà. Se tut - to il co - di - ce do - ves - si

B. & H. 15960

Exit Bartolo

Recitative

Marcellina

I shall not give up hope yet, if
Tut - to an - cor non ho per - so: mi

Enter Susanna

I can win my ac - tion. But here comes Su - san - na. I'll make a
re - sta la spe - ran - za. Ma Su - san - na si a - van - za. Io vò pro -

(as if to herself, but loudly)

start now, pre - tend - ing not to see her. So that's the pearl of
- var - mi, fin - giam di non ve - der - la. E quel - la buo - na

Susanna (aside)

vir - tue he pro - pos - es to wed! That's me she's
per - la la vo - reb - be spo - sar. Di me fa -

The Marriage of Figaro

Nº 5 Duettino (Susanna and Marcellina)

The Marriage of Figaro

The Marriage of Figaro

Recitative

Susanna

Old frump, how I de-test her! treating me like a school-girl, just be-
Va là, vec-chia pe-dan-te, dot-to-res-sa ar-ro-gan-te, perchè ha

Enter Cherubino **Cherubino**

-cause she gave les-sons to my la-dy be-fore she ran a-way. Ah, Su-san-na, 'tis
let-ti due li-bri, e sec-ca-ta ma-da-ma in gio-ven-tù. Su-san-net-ta, sei

Susanna **Cherubino**

you! 'Tis I. What do you want, sir? Oh, my
tu? Son io, co-sa vo-le-te? Ah, cor

Susanna **Cherubino**

sweetheart! a mis-for-tune! Your sweetheart? What has hap-pen'd His lordship
mi-o, che ac-ci-den-te! Cor vo-stro? co-sa av-ven-ne? Il Con-te

yes-ter-day found me all a-lone with Bar-ba-ri-na, and was fur-ious-ly
ie-ri, per-chè trovom-mi sol con Bar-ba-ri-na, il con-ge-do mi

ang - ry; and if our gra - cious la - dy, who's my god - mo - ther, can - not
aie - de; e se la Con - tes - si - na, la mia bel - la co - ma - re,

man - age to get me par - don'd, I'm sent a - way__ never more shall I behold my dear Su -
gra - zia non m'in - ter - ce - de, io va - do vi - a, io non ti ve - do più, Su - san - na

Susanna

- san - na! Ne - ver more be - hold me? Oh, dear! And so I was
mi - a. Non ve - de - te più me? Bra - vo! ma dun - que non

Cherubino

wrong when I im - ag - in'd that you were sigh - ing in secret for my la - dy? Ah! I
più per la Con - tes - sa se - cre - ta - men - te il vostro cor so - spi - ra? Ah, che

can but a - dore her at a dis - tance. I en - vy you, who see her as of - ten as you
trop - po ri - spet - to el - la m'in - spi - ra! Fe - li - ce te, che puo - i ve - der - la quando

Susanna: rib-bons! Not till my dy-ing day will I re-store it. How can you be so
na-strol Io non tel ren-de-rò che col-la vi-ta. Cos' è quest' in-so-

Cherubino: naugh-ty? Don't be so an-gry! A fair ex-change no rob-ber-y: here's a
-len-za? Eh via, sta che-ta. In ri-com-pen-sa, po-i, que-sta

song I will give you, that I've written. Susanna: What use is that to me, pray? Cherubino: Sing it, Su-san-na,
mia can-zo-net-ta io ti vò da-re. E che ne deb-bo fa-re? Leg-gi-la al-la pa-

sing it! Sing it be-fore my la-dy, sing it to Bar-ba-
-dro-na; leg-gi-la tu, me-des-ma, leg-gi-la a Bar-ba-

-ri-na, to Mar-cel-li-na, sing it to ev-'ry wo-man in the
-ri-na, a Mar-cel-li-na— leg-gi-la ad o-gni don-na del pa-

Susanna: cas-tle! Poor lit-tle Che-ru-bi-no, are you cra-zy?
-laz-zo! Po-ve-ro Che-ru-bin, sie-te voi paz-zo!

Nº 6 Aria

Allegro vivace

Cherubino

Is it pain, is it pleasure that fills me, And with fe-verish ec-sta-sy
Non so più co-sa son, co-sa fac-cio, or di fo-co, ora so-no di

thrills me? At the sight of a wo-man I trem-ble, And my heart seems to burst in-to
ghiac-cio, O-gni don-na cangiar di co-lo-re, o-gni don-na mi fa pal-pi-

flame, and my heart seems to burst in-to flame, and my heart seems to
-tar, o-gni don-na mi fa pal-pi-tar, o-gni don-na mi

burst in-to flame. Love! that word sets me hop-ing and fear-ing,
fa pal-pi-tar. So - lo ai no-mi d'amor di di-let-to,

Love! that word that I always am hear-ing! Love! ah love! how
mi si tur-ba, mi s'al-te-ra il pet-to, e a par-la-re mi

B.& H. 15960

52

The Marriage of Figaro

B. & H. 15960

Recitative

Ct. -mo - ment! You know the king's ap - point - ed me am - bas - sa - dor to
-ro - le: *tu sai che am - ba - scia - to - re a Lon - dra il Re mi di - chia-*

Ct. Lon - don. That means of course that Fi - ga - ro must go with me. **Susanna** My lord, I
-rò; *di con - dur me - co Fi - ga - ro de - sti - na - i. Si - gnor, se o-*

S. beg you— **Count** Ask me, ask what you will then; you know the pri - vi - lege that you can com-
-sas - si— *Par - la, par - la, mia ca - ra, e con quel drit - to ch' og - gi pren - di su*

Ct. -mand. For life I am your ser - vant; what could I re - fuse you? **Susanna** My lord, pray let me
me, *fin - che tu vi - vi chie - di, im - po - ni, pre - scri - vi. La - scia - te - mi, Si-*

S. go; to claim that pri - vi - lege is the last thing I wish for.
-gnor, *drit - ti non pren - do, non ne vò, non ne in - ten - do.*

S. You make me wretched. **Count** No, no, Su - san - na, I want to make you
Oh me in fe - li - ce! Ah nò, Su - san - na, io ti vò far fe-

The Marriage of Figaro   B. & H. 15960

Count
Susanna

that, sir! Hush now, and don't let him stop here. What next, I
-la - te. Ta - ci, e cer - ca,ch'ei par - ta. Ohi - me! che

(The Count hides behind the chair and Cherubino
scrambles round and sits in it. Susanna covers
him with a dress. Enter Basilio)
Basilio

won - der? Su - san - na, peace be
fa - te! Su - san - na, il ciel vi

Susanna

with you! I came to ask if you'd seen his lord-ship? And what should I know a-bout his
- sal - vi! A - vre-ste a ca - so ve-du-to il Con - te? E co - sa de - ve far me-co il

Basilio

lord-ship? Pray go a - way, sir. Wait a mo - ment; I tell you Fi - ga-ro
Con - te? a - ni-mo,u-sci - te. A-spet - ta - te, sen - ti - te, Fi - ga-ro

Susanna

wants to find him. In - deed, sir? To find the man who af-ter you most
di lui cer - ca. Oh cie - lo! Ei cer - ca chi, do - po voi, più

Count (aside)
Basilio

hates him? I'll hear now how he serves me. No, you are wrong; it does not always
l'o - dia. (Ve - diam co - me mi ser - ve.) Io non ho mai nel - la mo-ral sen -

B.& H. 15960

Bas.

fol - low that he who loves a man's wife should hate the la - dy's hus - band. My
-ti - to, ch'u - no ch'a - mi la mo - glie o - dii il ma - ri - to. Per

Susanna

Bas.

lord in fact a - dores you. How dare you come to me, sir, with these vile pro - po -
dir che il Con - te v'a - ma. Sor - ti - te, vil mi - ni - stro de l'al - trui sfre - na -

S.

-si - tions? I will not lis - ten to your talk of his lord-ship, his pas - sion,
-tez - za· io non ho d'uo - po del - la vo - stra mo - ra - le, del Con - te,

Basilio

S.

his de-sires— Oh, there's no harm done. 'Tis a mat - ter of taste, ma'am
del suo a-mor— Non c'è al - cun ma - le. Ha cia-scun i suoi gu - sti.

Bas.

yet I con - fess I im-ag-in'd that like ev-'ry other wo - man you would choose for a
Io mi cre - de a che pre-fe-rir do - ve-ste per a-man - te, co - me fan tut - te

Bas.

lo - ver one who's no-ble and rich, and quite dis-creet too, instead of yield-ing to a
quan - te un Si-gnor li - be-ral, pruden-te, e sag - gio, a un gio-vi-na-stro, a un

Susanna **Basilio**

page-boy— To Che-ru-bi-no? Yes, Che-ru-bi-no, your lit-tle Prince Charming!
pag-gio. *A Che-ru-bi-no?* *A Che-ru-bi-no,* *Che-ru-bin d'a-mo-re.*

Ear-ly this ve-ry morn-ing he was hov-'ring round a-bout here at your
Ch'og-gi sul far del gior-no *pas-seg-gia-va quì in-tor-no* *per en-*

Susanna **Basilio**

door. What a slan-der! all of your own in-vent-ing! Is it slan-der with you
-trar. Uom ma-li-gno, un' im-po-stu-ra è que-sta. *È un ma-li-gno con voi*

to keep one's eyes o-pen? And what a-bout that song, too? Tell me, between our
chi ha gli oc-chi in te-sta? *E quel-la can-zo-net-ta, di-te-mi in con-fi-*

-selves now— I need not say to you that I ne-ver repeat things— was it for you,
-den-za, io so-no a-mi-co, ed al-trui nul-la di-co, è per voi,

Susanna (aside) **Basilio**

or for my la-dy? Where did he pick up this then? By the way, too, Su-san-na,
per ma-da-ma? (Chi dia-vol glie l'ha det-to?) A pro-po-si-to, fi-glia,

Bas. 'twould be wise just to warn him; you've no i - dea how he gloats up-on my
in-stru-i - te-lo me - glio. *E - gli la guar-da a ta-vo-la si*

Bas. la - dy when he's wait-ing at ta - ble. If my lord were to no - tice— well, need I
spes - so, *e con ta-le im-mo-de-stia,* *che s'il Con - te s'ac-cor-ge— e sul tal*

Susanna

Bas. tell you? on that point he's quite a sa-vage. Oh, you monster! You are
pun - to, *sa - pe - te* *e-gli è una be - stia.* *Scel-le-ra-to!* *e per-*

Basilio

S. al-ways in-vent-ing lies and then spreading them broadcast. I? oh, you wrong me.
-chè an - da - te voi tai men-zo-gne spar-gen-do? Io! *che in-giu-sti - zia!*

Bas. All I did was to tell you what ev-'ry-bo-dy talks a-bout; I've
quel che com-pro io ven - do, *a quel che tut - ti di - co-no,* *io*

Count (coming forward) Basilio (aside) Susanna (aside)

Bas. ad-ded no-thing to it. Well, sir, what do they talk about? De-light-ful! Oh heavens!
non ag-giungo un pe-lo. *Co - me! che di-con tut-ti? (Oh bel-la!) Oh cie-lo!*

Nº 7 Trio (Susanna, Basilio, Count)

B.& H. 15960

The Marriage of Figaro

B. & H. 15960

Recitative

B. & H. 15960

The Marriage of Figaro

Nº 8 Chorus

Enter Peasants, followed by Figaro with a veil in his hand.

Allegro

Soprano
Alto

Come, lads and lass - es, flowers humbly strew - ing, And praise with
Gio - va - ni lie - te, fio - ri spar - ge - te, da - van - ti il

Tenor

Bass

thank - ful hearts our gracious lord; Fair - er than all is
no - bi - le no - stro Si - gnor. Il suo gran co - re

that flow'r of vir - tue, which to our land of love... he..... has re -
vi ser - ba in - tat - to, d'un più bel fio...... re..... l'al - mo can -

The Marriage of Figaro

Recitative

first hap-py bride-groom to ob-tain the ad-van-tage of your de-cree. This ve-ry
vo-stra sag-gez-za il pri-mo frut-to og-gi no-i co-glie-rem: le no-stre

day Su-san-na and I are to be mar-ried; so may it please you, since by
noz-ze si son già sta-bi-li-te, or a voi toc-ca co-

your grace I re-ceive her as a vir-tu-ous bride, to place with your own
-stei che un vo-stro do-no il-li-ba-ta ser-bò, co-prir di que-sta,

hands up-on her head this sym-bol of vir-tue. They're cle-ver at plot-ting;
sim-bo-lo d'o-ne-sta, can-di-da ve-sta. (Dia-bo-li-ca a-stu-zia!

Count (aside)

(Aloud)
I'll not be ta-ken in. My friends, I thank you for your loy-al de-
ma fin-ge-re con-vien.) Son gra-to, a-mi-ci, ad un sen-so si o-

-vo-tion; it was on-ly my du-ty to re-form these a-bu-ses,
-ne-sto! ma non mer-to per que-sto, ne tri-bu-ti, nè lo-di,

The Marriage of Figaro

B.& H. 15960

80

Nᵒ 8ª Chorus

 B. & H. 15960

Recitative

B. & H. 15960

№ 9 Aria

F. white like a girl's tho' your face is, You must lose all your ring-lets and curls, you must
chio-ma, quell'a - ria bril-lan - te, *quel ver - mi - glio don-ne-sco co - lor,* *quel ver-*

F. lose all your ring-lets and curls. Not for you are frills and
-mi-glio don-ne-sco co-lor. *Non più a-vrai* *quei pen-nac-*

F. fea-thers, curls and ring-lets, airs and gra-ces, and sweet pret-ty
-chi-ni, *quel cap-pel-lo,* *quel-la chio-ma,* *quell'a - ria bril-*

F. fa-ces. Say good-bye now to pas-time and play, lad. Say good-bye to your airs and your
-lan-te! Non più andrai, far-fal-lo - ne a-mo - ro - so, *not - te e gior - no d'intor - no gi-*

F. gra-ces. Here's an end to the life that was gay, lad. Here's an end to your games with the
-ran-do, del - le bel - le tur-ban-do il ri - po - so, *Nar-ci-set - to, A-don-ci - no d'a-*

B. & H. 15960

girls, Here's an end to your romps in the hay, lad, Here's an end to your games with the
-mor, del - le bel - le tur-ban-do il ri - po - so, Nar - ci - set - to, A-don-ci - no d'a-
ten.

girls. Chest thrown out and shoulders back, sir!
-mor! Fra guer - rie - ri, pof - far Bac - co!

Hold your head up, not so slack, sir! Take your musket on your shoulder, That's the
Gran mus-tac-chi, stret-to sac - co, schiop-po in spal-la, scia-bla al fian-co, col - lo

right style for a sol - dier, Du-ty calls you to death or glo - ry; As to
drit - to, mu-so fran-co, o un gran ca - sco, o un gran tur - ban - te, mol-to o-

pay that's an-other sto - ry, quite an-oth-er sto-ry, quite an-oth-er sto-ry. No more
-nor, po - co con-tan - te, po - co con-tan - te, po - co con-tan-te. Ed in

The Marriage of Figaro

B. & H. 15960

90

The Marriage of Figaro

B. & H. 1596O

Some day you'll come back vic-tor-ious
Che - ru - bi-no,al - la vit-to-ria,

If you don't get kill'd be - fore;
al - la glo-ria mi - li - tar,

Then you'll
Che - ru-

swear that war is glo-rious,
- bi-no,al - la vit-to-ria,

Oh a glor - ious thing is war,
al - la glo - ria mi - li-tar,

Oh a
al - la

glor - ious thing is war,
glo - ria mi - li-tar,

Oh a glor - ious thing is war.
al - la glo - ria mi - li - tar!

End of Act I
B. & H. 15960

ACT II

The Countess's Boudoir   A door R.H., Closet L.H.   At the back a door leading to the servants' rooms.   At the side a window   Susanna discovered with the Countess.   She appears to have told the Countess something painful; the Countess makes a gesture of disgust and resignation, and Susanna goes to her room.

Nº 10 Cavatina

Larghetto

B. & H. 15960

The Marriage of Figaro

94

Recitative

Re-enter Susanna carrying a dress.

buy back in se-cret that old pri-vi-lege of the Lord of the Man-or. You
-men - te ri-cu-pe-rar vor-ri - a il di - rit - to feu-da - le; pos-

see it's ve - ry pos-si-ble and ve-ry na-tu-ral. Ve-ry pos-si-ble? Ve-ry
si - bi-le è la co - sa e na-tu - ra - le. Pos - si - bil? Na-tu-

Countess **Susanna**

na - tu-ral? Per-fect-ly na - tu-ral, and if Su-san-na's wil - ling, per-fect-ly
-ral? Na - tu - ra-lis - si - ma, e, se Su-san - na vuol, pos - si - bi -

Figaro

pos - si-ble. Have done with all your talk - ing! I've done al-rea - dy.
-lis - si - ma. Fi - ni - sci - la u - na vol - ta, Ho già fi - ni - to.

Susanna **Figaro**

That was why he de-cid - ed to take me to Lon - don as cour-ier, and choose Su
Quin - di pre-se il par-ti - to, di sce-glier - me cor - rie - ro, e la Su-

-san - na 'con-fi-den-tial at-tach-ée to the em-bas-sy'; and be-cause she per
-san - na con-si-glie - ra se-cre-ta d'am-ba - scia - ta; e perch' el - la o-sti-

B. & H. 1596

-sis-tent-ly re-fu-ses the di-plo-ma-tic post which she was of-fer'd, he
na-ta o-gnor ri-fiu-ta il di-plo-ma d'o-nor, ch'ei le de-sti-na, mi-

threatens now to fav-our Mar-cel-li-na. Now you know the whole sto-ry. Have you the
nac-cia di pro-teg-ger Mar-cel-li-na; que-sto è tut-to l'af-fa-re. Ed hai co-

Susanna

heart to speak of this so light-ly? 'Tis a se-ri-ous mat-ter. Aren't you
-rag-gio di trat-tar scher-zan-do un ne-go-zio si se-rio? Non vi

Figaro

thank-ful that I can take it so light-ly? Hear what I've
ba-sta, che scher-zan-do io ci pen-si? ec-co il pro-

done now; I have sent by Ba-si-lio an an-o-ny-mous let-ter to warn him a-bout an as-sig-
-get-to: per Ba-si-lio un bi-gliet-to io gli fo ca-pi-tar, che l'av-ver-ti-sca di cer-to ap-pun-ta-

-na-tion to be giv-en to-night to a lov-er by my la-dy. Oh heav'ns,
-men-to, che per l'o-ra del bal-lo a un a-man-te voi de-ste. O ciel!

Countess

The Marriage of Figaro

B. & H. 15960

Figaro

Cts.

how could you?   To a man who's so jea - ious!   So much the bet - ter;   that
che sen - to!   ad un uom si ge - lo - so—   An - co - ra me - glio,   co -

F.

makes it eas - ier still to set him wond-'ring,   to har-rass him, to em - broil him,
-sì po - trem più pre - sto im-ba-raz-zar - lo,   con - fon - der - lo,   im-bro-gliar - lo,

F.

to up-set all his pro - jects,   to   fill him with sus - pi - cion,   to make him
ro - ve-sciar-gli i pro-get - ti,   em - pier - lo di so-spet - ti,   e por-gli in

F.

rea - lize   that the game he is play - ing   is a game o-ther peo-ple can play up-on
te - sta, che la mo-der - na   fe - sta   ch'ei di fa - re a me ten - ta,   al - tri a lui

F.

him too. We'll make him waste all the day   in search   of the cul - prit,   and
fac - cia;   on - de quà per - da il tem-po, i - vi   la   trac - cia,   co -

F.

then, all of a sud-den, be-fore his no - ble   lord-ship can in - ter-fere with our de-
-sì, qua - si ex ab - rup - to, e sen - za ch'ab-bia   fat - to per fra-stor-nar - ci al - cun di -

- sign, he will find us getting married; and then I think he'll see that op-po-si-tion would be
-se - gno vien l'o-ra del-le noz - ze, in fac-cia a lei non fia, ch'o-si d'op-por-si ai vo - ti

Susanna

use-less. May be, but you are reck-on-ing with-out Mar-cel-li - na. One
mie - i. È ver, ma in di lui ve - ce s'op-por - rà Mar-cel-li - na. A-

Figaro

mo - ment— I have it! You'll let his lord-ship know that he can
-spet - ta, al Con - te fa - rai su - bi - to dir, che ver - so

meet you this ev - 'ning in the gar - den. We'll dress up Che - ru -
se - ra at - ten-da-ti in giar - di - no; il pic - ciol Che - ru -

-bi - no (I took good care that he should not de - part yet,) dress him up as a
-bi - no, per mio con - si - glio non an - cor par - ti - to, da fem-mi - na ve -

wo - man, and send him to the gar - den to keep your ap-point-ment. In the
sti - to, fa - re - mo che in sua ve - ce i - vi sen va - da; que-sta è

F. If my lord's af-ter a lit-tle a-musement, he may go danc-ing, but
Se vuol bal - la..... re, si - gnor Con - ti - no, il chi - tar - ri - no,

Allegretto

F. I'll play the tune, yes, I'll play the tune, yes, I'll play the tune.
le suo - ne - rò, si, le suo - ne - rò, si, le suo - ne - rò.

Exit.

Recitative

Countess

I'm not hap-py, Su - san-na, to think that Che - ru -
Quan - to duol - mi, Su - san - na, che que - sto gio - vi -

-bi - no heard all the things that his lord-ship said this
- not - to ab - bia del Con - te le stra - va - gan - ze u -

morn - ing. You can't im - a - gine— Why did he go to
- di - to! ah! tu non sa - i— ma per qual cau - sa

is in - deed! As if you meant it! Make haste, and sing the
si, cer - to! I - po - cri - to - ne! via pre - sto la can

song now that you gave me this morning; let her la - dy-ship hear it. Who wrote the
- zo - ne, che sta - ma - ne a me de - ste, a ma - da - ma can - ta - te. Chi n'è l'au -

Countess

Susanna

song? Who wrote it? You need not ask him when he's blush - ing all
- tor? Guar - da - te, e-gli ha due bra - ce di ros - sor sul - la

Countess   **Cherubino**

o - ver. Take my guitar, Su - san - na, and play it for him. I
fac - cia. Pren - di la mia chi - tar - ra, e l'ac-com-pa - gna. Io

Susanna

trem - ble with e - mo - tion, but if my la - dy wish - es— She
so - no sì tre - man - te— ma se ma-da - ma vuo - le— Lo

does in - deed; you hear, don't keep her wait - ing.
vuo - le, sì, lo vuol, man - co pa - ro - le.

Nº 11 Canzona

You... know young Cu - pid,... Is this his dart? You... know young
Don - ne, ve - de - te,..... s'io l'ho nel cor, don - ne, ve -

Cu - pid,... Is this his... dart?
de - te,..... s'io l'ho nel cor!

Recitative

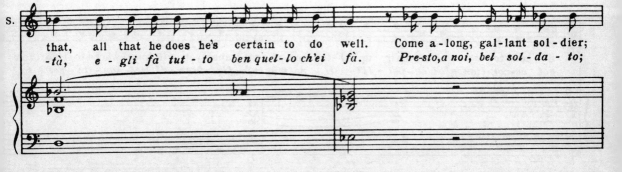

Countess   **Susanna**

Bra - vo! your voice is charming; I ne-ver knew that you could sing so agreeably. Oh, as to
Bra - vo! che bel-la vo - ce, io non sa - pe - a che can - ta - ste si be - ne. Oh in ve - ri -

that, all that he does he's certain to do well. Come a - long, gal - lant sol - dier;
- tà, e - gli fà tut - to ben quel-lo ch'ei fà. Pre-sto, a noi, bel sol - da - to;

The Marriage of Figaro

Nᵒ 12 Aria

talking aria

Allegretto Susanna

Come here, and kneel be-fore me now,
Ve - ni-te in-gi-noc-chia-te-vi,

Keep qui-et if you can; keep qui-et, keep qui-et, keep qui-et if you
re-sta-te fer-mo lì, re-sta-te, re-sta-te, re-sta-te fer-mo

stay there

can, keep qui-et if you can.
lì, re-sta-te fer-mo lì.

And now just turn your
Pian, pia no or via gi-

face away, That's right! that suits my plan.
-ra-te-vi. bra-vo! va ben co - sì.

Come,
La

turn full face to-wards me now,
fac-cia o-ra vol-ge-te-mi,

To me, not o-ver
O-là! que gli oc-chi a

B. & H. 15980

114

Recitative

Countess
Real - ly, you are too sil - ly.
Quan - te buf - fo - ne - ri - e!

Susanna
I'm half a - fraid I am go-ing to be jea - lous.
Ma se ne so - no io me-des - ma ge-lo - sa!

S. (to Cherubino)
You lit - tle mis - chief, how dare you have the face to be so
Eh! ser - pen - tel - lo, vo - le - te tra - la-sciar d'es - ser si

S.
pret - ty? Su - san - na, no more non-sense! I think you'll have to pull up his
bel - lo? Fi - niam le ra - gaz - za - te; or quel - le ma - ni - che ol - tre il

Countess

Cts.
sleeves to the el - bow; then they will not be in the way when you put his
go - mi - to gli al - za, on - de più a - gia - ta - men - te l'a - bi - to gli si a -

Cts.

Susanna
dress on. I see.
-dat - ti. Ec - co.

Countess
Still high - er! That's right. What is that
Più in - die - tro, co - sì. Che na-stro è

The Marriage of Figaro

B. & H. 15960

Exit Susanna

Cts.
there; it's in the cup-board. A-bout that rib-bon— I think I'd like to
-tà, ch'è sul-lo scri-gno, in quan-to al na-stro— in ver— per il co-

Re-enter Susanna   Susanna

Cts.
keep it; it's a co-lour that suits me. Here's plas-ter; and we shall want a
-lo-re mi spia-ce di pri-var-me-ne. Te-ne-te, e da le-gar gli il

Countess (to Susanna)   Cherubino

S.
ban-dage. Then as you're go-ing, fetch an- o-ther piece of rib-bon. No,
brac-cio? Un al-tro na-stro pren-di in-siem col mio ve-sti-to. Ah,

Countess

C.
'tis that piece that a-lone could have heal'd me. But why? this bit is
più pre-sto m'a-vria quel-lo gua-ri-to! Per-chè? que-sto è mi-

Cherubino

Cts.
clean-er. But I've a feel-ing— that if a rib-bon— has touch'd the hair of
-glio-re. Al-lor che un na-stro— le-gò la chio-ma— ov-ver toc-cò la

Countess

C.
some-one— some per-son— who's a stran-ger, it has a power of heal-ing! Do you
pel-le— d'og-get-to— Fo-re-stie-ro, è buon per le fe-ri-te, non è

The Marriage of Figaro

B. & H. 15960

B. & H. 15960

some-thing. Pray, ma - dam, read this let - ter. Hea - vens! 'tis Fi - ga - ro's a
-quil - la, guar - da - te que - sto fo - glio. Nu - mi! è il fo - glio che

- no - nymous let - ter. What's mak-ing all that noise in there? I think it's something fal - len
Fi - ga - ro gli scris - se. Cos' è co - de - sto stre - pi - to? in ga - bi - net - to qual - che

down in your dressing-room. I did not no - tice a - ny - thing. It's clear enough you're pre - oc - cu - pied and
co - sa è ca - du - ta, io non in - te - si nien - te. Con - vien che abbia - te i gran pensieri in

anxious. Am I? Some-one's in - side there. Who do you think it is then?
men - te. Di che? La v'è qual - cu - no. Chi vo - le - te che si - a?

That you can tell me; I've on - ly just come in here. Ah, yes, Su -
Lo chie - do a vo - i; io ven - go in que - sto pun - to. Ah - si - Su -

Nº 13 Terzetto Susanna, Countess, Count

B. & H. 15960

124

The Marriage of Figaro

B. & H. 1596

The Marriage of Figaro

The Marriage of Figaro

The Marriage of Figaro

Recitative

Count: You'll not un-lock the door, ma'am? **Countess:** And pray, why should I, When the room is my own?
Dun-que voi non a-pri-te? E per-chè deg-gio le mie ca-me-re a-prir?

Count: Just as it suits you; then I'll have the door forced. Ho,
Eb-ben la-scia-te, l'a-pri-rem sen-za chia-ve; ehi,

Countess (restraining him): you there! What, sir! do you propose to ques-tion my hon-our in pub-lic? **Count:** I was
gen-te. Co-me? por-re-ste a re-pen-ta-glio d'u-na da-ma l'o-no-re? È

has-ty, I grant you. It shall all be done qui-et-ly; I will not have a
ve-ro, io sba-glio, pos-so sen-za ru-mo-re, Sen-za scan-da-lo al

scan-dal be-fore the ser-vants. I'll go my-self now and fetch the tools to
-cun di no-stra gen-te, an-dar io stes-so a pren-der l'oc-cor-

The Marriage of Figaro

Nº 14 Duet Susanna, Cherubino

Allegro assai

Susanna

Be quick, un-lock the door now, It's on-ly me, Su - san-na; Come quick-ly, come
A - pri - te, pre-sto a-pri-te, a - pri - te, è la Su - san - na, sor - ti - te, sor-

quick-ly, come quickly, oh, come quick-ly, No long-er must you stay. No long-er must you
- ti - te, sor - ti - te, via sor - ti - te, an - da - te via di quà. An - da - te via di

Enter Cherubino from dressing room

stay. Be quick, be
quà. Di quà, di

Cherubino

Su - san - na, 'tis too ter - ri - ble, Do help me now, I pray.
Oi - mè! che sce-na or - ri - bi - le! Che gran fa - ta - li - tà!

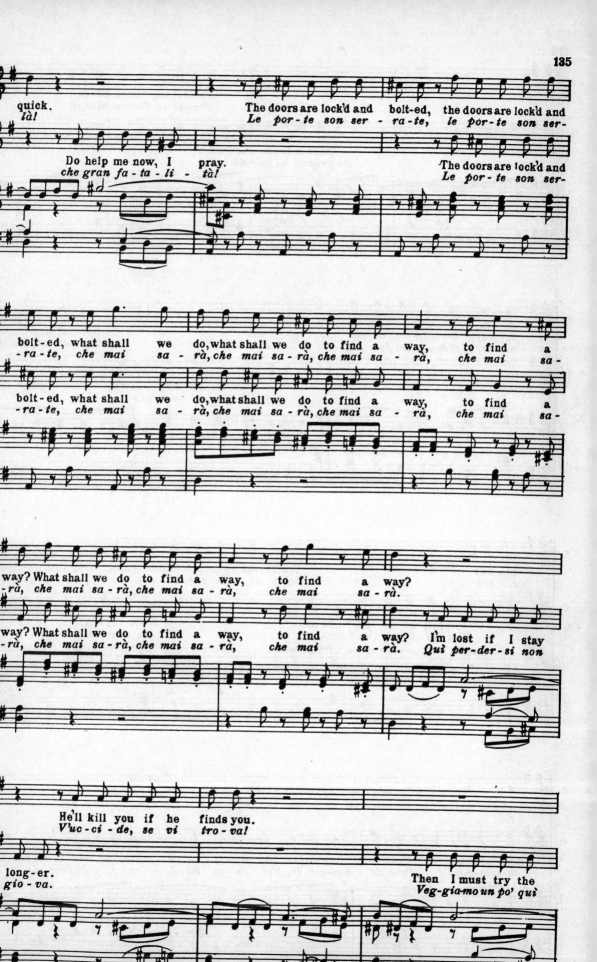

136

The Marriage of Figaro

B. & H. 159

(Cherubino jumps out of the window)

He'll break his neck for
Ei va a pe - ri - re, o

(kisses Susanna)

-sire..... so kiss her and say good - bye!
le - i. *Ad - di - o!* *co - sì si fa!*

certain. Not that way,'tis to high! Che-ru-bi - no, Che-ru-bi - no!
De - il Fer - ma - te, per pie - tà! *Fer - ma - te, fer - ma - te!*

cresc.

f

Recitative

Susanna (at the window looking after Cherubino)

Look at the lit - tle ras - cal, how he's run - ning! He's a
Oh guar-da il de - mo - niet - to co - me fug - ge! *è già un*

mile off al - rea - dy. No time for me to lose now; I'll
mi - glio lon - ta - no; *Ma non per-diam-ci in - va - no;* *en -*

slip in - to the dress-ing room. Pray come in, jealous hus-band! I'm rea-dy
-triam nel ga - bi - net - to; *Ven - ga poi lo smargias-so;* *io qui l'as-*

The Marriage of Figaro

lis - ten. Then it is not Su - san - na? No, there's some - bo - dy else there,
-quil - lo. *Non è dun - que Su - san - na?* *No,* *ma in - ve - ce è un og - get - to,*

one whose harm - less in - ten - tions you've no right to sus - pect. I was pre -
che ra - gion di so - spet - to *non vi de - ve la - sciar:* *per que - sta*

-par - ing for this eve - ning's a - muse - ment a harm - less piece of
se - ra *u - na bur - la in - no - cen - te* *di far - si di - spo -*

fool - ing, and I will swear to you, I have done noth - ing wrong. Who
-ne - va, *ed io vi giu - ro* *che l'o - nor —* *l'o - nes - tà —* *Chi è*

is it? tell me! I'll have his blood! Oh lis - ten! I can - not
dun - que? *di - te — l'uc - ci - de - rò.* *Sen - ti - te, (ah non ho*

Nº 15 Finale

B. & H. 15960

-voke some fa-tal deed, 'twill pro-voke some fa - tal deed.
-ces-so gli fa far, qual-che ec-ces - so gli fa far.

this I'll make him bleed, I'll make him bleed.
-gion del mio pe - nar, del mio pe - nar.

door; finds Susanna standing in the doorway

(astonished)

Su-san-na!
Su-san-na!

Su-san-na!
Su-san-na!

Molto andante

Susanna

Your ser-vant! But why this a-maze-ment? If
Si - gno - re! Cos' è quel stu-po - re? Il

you're still in-tend-ing to kill Che-ru-bi-no, you see him be-fore you, the
bran-do pren-de-te, il pag-gio uc-ci-de-te! Quel pag-gio mal-na-to Ve-

trai-tor...'twas me!.... you see him be-fore you, the trai-tor 'twas me!
-de - te - lo quà, quel pag-gio mal-na-to ve-de-te-lo quà.

B. & H. 15960

150

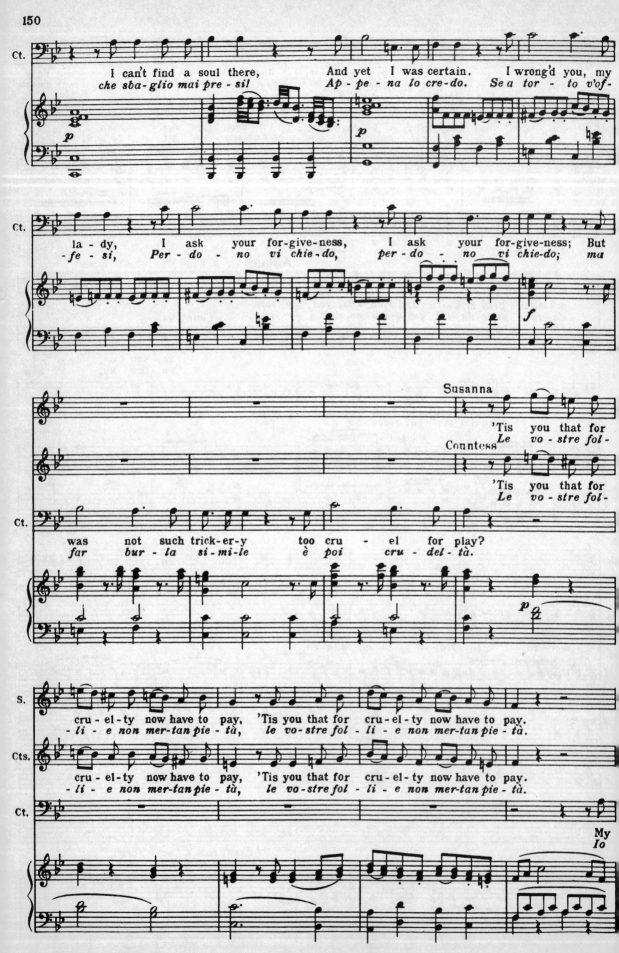

I scorn you! *Nol di-te!* De-ceiv-er! *men-ti-te!* You swore you'd re-*Son l'em-pia, l'in-*

dear-est! *v'a-mo!* I love you. *vel giu-ro!*

-nounce me, *-fi-da,* As faith-less de-nounce me. *Che o-gno-ra v'in-gan-na.*

Oh help me, Su-san-na, *Quell' i-ra, Su-san-na,* Oh, *M'a-*

Susanna

To doubt and sus-pi-cion you should not give way; Let this be a *Co-sì... si con-dan-na chi può sos-pet-tar, co-sì si con-*

what can I say? *-i-ta a cal-mar.*

S.

warn-ing to you from to-day. *-dan-na chi può so-spet-tar.* Countess

For years of de-vo-tion *A-dun-que la fe-de* so pa-tient and faith-ful. *d'un' a-ni-ma a-man-te,*

Cts.
Shall I be re-ward-ed with doubt and dis-may?
Si fie - ramer - ce - de do - ve - va spe - rar?

Count
Oh, help me, Su-
Quell' i - ra, Su-

Susanna
To doubt and sus- pi- cion you should not give
Co - sì... si con - dan-na chi può... so-spet-

Ct.
- san - na, Oh, what can I say?
- san - na, m'a - i - ta a cal-mar.

S.
way. Let this be a warn-ing to you from to-day.
-tar, co-sì si con-dan-nu chi può so-spet-tar.

My la - dy!
Si - gno - ra!

Countess
How can you re-mind me of those days?
Cru - de - le! più quel - la non so - no!

Count
Ro - si - na!
Ro - si - na!

B. & H. 15964

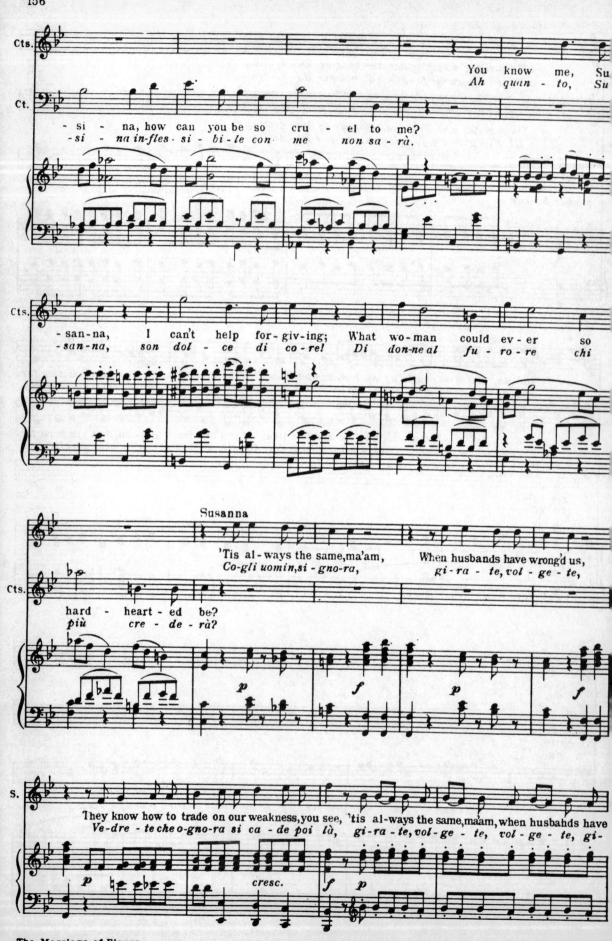

wrong'd us, they know how to trade on our weakness, you see.
-ra - te, ve-dre-te che ogno-ra si ca - de poi là.

Countess

Count
For shame, sir!
In - gra - to!

For - give.... me!
Guar - da - te-mi!

For -
Guar -

For shame, sir!
In - gra - to!

- give..... me!
- da - te-mi!

For - give...... me, I've wrong'd you; and re-
Guar - da - te-mi, ho tor - to, e mi

Susanna
sotto voce

And now   all is ov- er, was
Da que - sto mo - men-to, Quest'

sotto voce

And now all is ov- er, was
Da que - sto mo - men-to, Quest'

sotto voce

- pent it.
pen - to.

And now all is ov- er, was
Da que - sto mo - men-to, Quest'

con Ped.

The Marriage of Figaro

B. & H. 15960

Allegro

The Marriage of Figaro

The Marriage of Figaro

The Marriage of Figaro

B.& H. 15

The Marriage of Figaro

B. & H. 15960

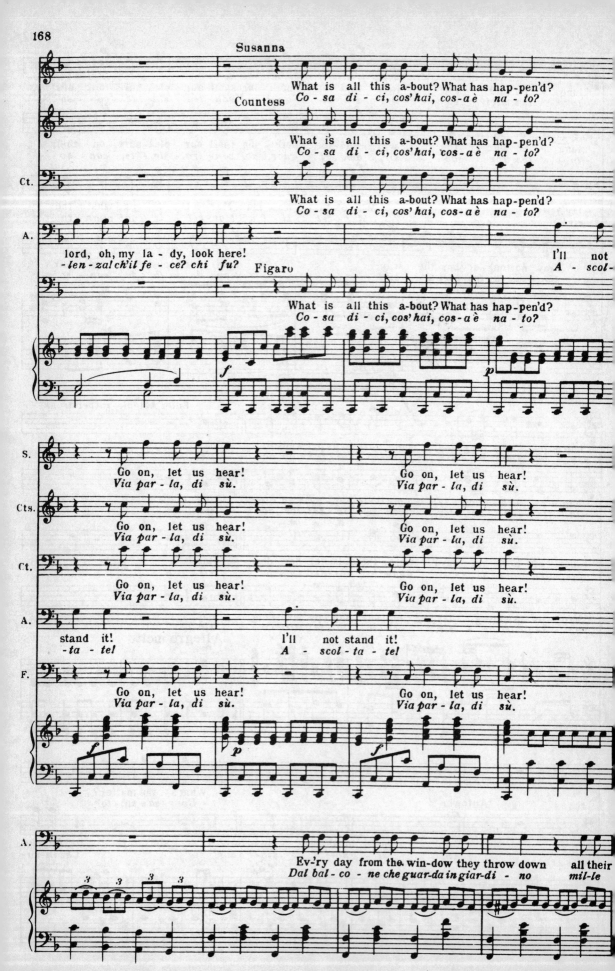

B. & H. 1596

The Marriage of Figaro

176

The Marriage of Figaro

B. & H. 1590

178

The Marriage of Figaro

B. & H. 15960

The Marriage of Figaro

(tearing up the paper)

Ct. Oh, the / Que - sto

F. Well, it's u - sual to seal a com - mis - sion.
E l'u - san - za di por - vi il su - gel - lo.

Susanna
If we wea-ther the storm now in safe - -
Se mi sal - vo da que - sta tem - pe - -

Countess
If we wea-ther the storm now in
Se mi sal - vo da que - sta tem -

Ct. ras - cal's too much for my pa - tience. There is
bir - bo mi to - glie il cer - vel - lo, Tut - to,

F. You may blu-ster and rage as you
Sbuf-fa in - va - no e la ter - ra cal -

S. - - - - - - - - - ty, If we
- - - - - - - - - sta, se mi

- safe - ty, we shall not have a ship-wreck to fear. If we
- pe - sta, più non hav - vi nau - fra - gio per me. se mi

Ct. some - thing con - ceal'd from me here. Oh, the
tut to è un mi - ste - ro per me. que - sto

F. like, sir. But I know more than you do, it's clear. You may
- pe - sta, po - ve - ri - no, ne sa men di me! sbuf - fa in-

The Marriage of Figaro

184

The Marriage of Figaro

B.& H. 159

The Marriage of Figaro

B. & H. 1596

Count

I for-bid these in-ter-rup-tions;
Pian, pia-nin, sen - za schia-maz-zi,

sure - ly are, all three.
mai ven-go-no a far?

Ct.

Let them state their case to me, let them state their case to
Di - ca o-gnun quel che gli par, di - ca o-gnun quel che gli

Marcellina

This man here has sign'd a con-tract, sign'd a con-tract to es-
Un im - pe-gno nu-zi - a - le ha co-stui con me con-

Ct.

me.
par.

M.

pouse me, and I make an ap-pli-ca-tion, that the contract be ful-fill'd.
trat - to, e pre-ten-do ch'il con-trat-to de - va me-co ef-fet-tu - ar.

B. & H. 15960

The Marriage of Figaro

S. — for - tunes we're sur rounded; 'Twas the de - vil,.... I.... am
-ra - ta, sba-lor-di-ta; Cer-to un dia-vol dell' in-

Cts. — for - tunes we're sur-round-ed; 'Twas the de - vil,.... I.... am
-ra - ta, sba-lor-di-ta; Cer-to un dia-vol dell' in-

M. We'll soon make him look de - jec-ted;
E cre-sciu-to a tut - ti il na-so;

Bas. We'll soon make him look de - jec-ted;
E cre-sciu-to a tut - ti il na-so;

B. We'll soon make him look de - jec-ted;
E cre-sciu-to a tut ti il na-so;

Ct. We'll soon make him look de - jec-ted;
E cre-sciu-to a tut - ti il na-so;

F. — for - tunes we're sur-round-ed; 'Twas the
-ra - to,.. sba-lor - di - to: Cer - to un

S. cer-tain, sent these peo-ple here just now.... 'Twas the de-vil.. sent these peo-ple here just
-fer - no quì li ha fat-ti ca-pi - tar...... Cer- to un dia-vol quì li ha fat-ti ca-pi-

Cts. cer-tain, sent these peo-ple here just now.... 'Twas the de-vil.. sent these peo-ple here just
-fer - no quì li ha fat-ti ca-pi - tar...... Cer- to un dia-vol quì li ha fat-ti ca-pi-

M. ·It was real - ly..... pro - vi - den - tial That we
qual - che nu - me a noi pro-pi - zio, quì ci ha

Bas. It was real - ly pro - vi - den - tial That we
qual - che nu - me a noi pro-pi - zio, quì ci ha

B. It was real - ly pro - vi - den - tial That they
qual - che nu - me a noi pro-pi - zio, quì li ha

Ct. It was real - ly pro - vi - den - tial That we
qual - che nu - me a noi pro-pi - zio, quì ci ha

F. de - vil I am cer - tain, sent these peo-ple here just
dia - vol dell' in - fer - no quì li ha fat-ti ca-pi-

The Marriage of Figaro

The Marriage of Figaro

The Marriage of Figaro

196

The Marriage of Figaro

The Marriage of Figaro

B. & H. 1596

202

B. & H. 15960

The Marriage of Figaro

A large hall in the palace.
The Count alone, walking to and fro

ACT III

Recitative

Count

What a strange sit-u-a-tion! an a-no-ny-mous let-ter, and then the maid lock'd up in-side the
Che imba-razzo è mai questo! un fo-glio a-no-ni-mo, la ca-me-rie-ra in ga-bi-net-to

dressing room, with my la-dy so em-barrass'd— a man who jumps in-to the garden from the window,
chiu-sa, la pa-dro-na con-fu-sa— un uom' che sal-ta dal bal-co-ne in giar-di-no,

and then an-oth-er who says 'twas he that did so— what on earth can it mean? Could it have
un' al-tro ap-pres-so, che di-ce es-ser quel des-so; non so co-sa pen-sar, po-treb-be

been some young man of my dependants? there is no lim-it to what they will dare. But then the
for-se qual-cun de' miei vas-sa-li, a si-mil raz-za è com-mu-ne l'ar-dir, ma la Con-

Count-ess— no, I will not in-sult her; she has too high a sense of her
-tes-sa— ah, che un dub-bio l'of-fen-de! el-la ri-spet-ta trop-po se

dig-ni-ty, in-deed of mine too! Yes, mine too! Hu-man nat-ure is
stes-sa, e l'o-nor mi-o— l'o-no-re— Do-ve dia-min l'ha

The Marriage of Figaro

206

The Countess looks in and softly brings Susanna after her

(goes off up stage)

Countess (in a breathless whisper to Susanna)

Ct. frail, I must ad-mit it! / *po - sto u - ma - no er - ro - re!*
There, don't be fright-en'd; tell him / *Via! fat - ti co - re, di - gli*

Cts. to meet you in the gar-den. I won-der if Che-ru-bi-no ev-er went t / *che ti at-ten - da in giar-di - no, Sa - prò, se Che-ru-bi - no e-ra giun - to a S*

Count (to himself)

Ct. Se-ville? I've told Ba-si-lio to find out a-bout it. But, ma-dam, if / *-vi - glia, a ta - le og-get-to ho man-da-to Ba - si - lio. O cie - lo! e*

Susanna

S. Fi-ga-ro— Don't say a word to Fi-ga-ro! This as-sig-na-tion shall be / *Fi - ga-ro? A lui non dei dir nul - la, in ve-ce tu - a vo-glio a*

Countess

Cts. kept by my-self. Be-fore this ev-'ning Ba-si-lio will be back. My / *-dar-ci io me-de-sma. A - van-ti se - ra do-vreb-be ri-tor-nar. O*

Count

Susanna

S. la - dy, I dare not. Re-mem-ber, all my hap-pi-ness de-pends on it. And S / *Di - o! non o-so— Pen-sa ch'è in tua ma-no il mio ri-po-so. E S*

Countess

(exit)

Count

The Marriage of Figaro

B. & H. 15

-san - na? who knows? she may have told her la - dy-ship all I said to her;
-san - na? chi sa, ch'el - la tra - di - to ab - bia il se - gre - to mi - o,

oh! if she has done, he shall mar - ry the old la - dy! Mar-cel -
oh, se ha par - la - to, gli fo spo - sa la vec - chia. (Mar-cel -

Susanna (aside)

- li - na! My lord! And what do you want? My lord, have I of -
- li - na!) Si - gnor! Co - sa bra - ma - te? Mi par che sie - te in

(to Count) Count Susanna

-fend - ed you? Come, tell me, what's your bus -'ness? My lord, my la - dy
col - le - ra! Vo - le - te qual - che co - sa? Si - gnor, la vo-stra

Count Susanna

sent me - she's suf-f'ring from the va - pours, and de-sires you would
spo - sa ha i so - li - ti va - po - ri e vi chie - de il va -

lend her your smel-ling-bot-tle. Pray take it. I'll bring it back soon. No,
-set - to de - gli o - do - ri, Pren - de - te. Or vel ri - por - to. Ah

Count Susanna Count

the Marriage of Figaro

Ct.

no, pray keep it, you may want it your-self.
no; po-te-te ri-te-ner-lo per voi.

Susanna

My-self? girls in my po-
Per- me? que-sti non son

S.

- si-tion don't have ail-ments of that sort.
ma- li da don-ne tri-via-li.

Count

Not ev-en a girl who lost her
Un' a-man-te che per-de il ca-ro

Ct.

Susanna

bride-groom an hour be-fore the wed-ding?
spo- so sul pun-to d'ot-te-ner-lo.

We'll pay off Mar-cel-li-na with the dow-ry
Pa- gan-do Mar-cel-li-na col-le do-te

S.

that you so kind-ly pro-mis'd.
che voi mi pro-met-te-ste.

Count

You say I pro-mis'd? when pray?
Ch'io vi pro-mi-si! quan-do?

Susanna

I thought I un-der-
Cre- dea d'a-ver-lo in-

Count

S.

stood so. Yes, if you'd been in-clin'd to come to an un-der-stand-ing.
-te- so. Si, se vo-lu-to a-ve-ste in-ten-der-mi voi stes-sa.

Susanna

If that is
E mio do-

S.

all, sir, I hope I know my du-ty to-wards your lord-ship.
-ve- re, e quel di sua Eccel-len-za è il mio vo-le-re.

B. & H. 15980

Nº 16 **Duet** Susanna and The Count

B & H. 1596

The Marriage of Figaro

The Marriage of Figaro

Recitative

Count: Tell me, why did you treat me so se-vere-ly this morn-ing?
E per-chè fo-sti me-co sta mat-ti-na si au-ste-ra?

Susanna: With Che-ru-bi-no list-'ning?
Col pag-gio ch'i-vi ce-ra?

Count: You were no kind-er to Ba-si-lio, I know.
Ed a Ba-si-lio, che per me ti par-lò?

Susanna: What need have we of a man like Ba-si-lio?
Ma qual bi-so-gno abbiam noi, che un Ba-si-lio—

Count: You're right there, I
È ve-ro, è

214

Nº 17 Recitative and Aria

I'll wait no long-er.
il col-po è fat-to.

Allegro maestoso

Must
Ve-

I for-go my pleasure, While serf of mine re - joic - es?
-drò, mentr' io so - spi-ro, fe - li-ce un ser - vo mi - ol

Must I renounce my passion,
E un ben che in-van de - si - o,

He have his heart's de-sire? Must I be-hold my charmer To
ei pos-se-der do - vrà? Ve-drò per man d'a - mo - re u -

B. & H. 15960

laugh at me, yes, laugh at me While I............ am... mor - ti - ci -
ri - de - re, per ri - de - re Di mia in - fe - li - ci -

- fied? I will en-dure no long-er, Vengeance a-lone in-
- tà. Già la spe-ran - za so - la del - le ven-det - te

- spires me, 'Tis ven-geance, on - ly ven-geance Can sa - tis-fy my
mi - e quest' a - ni - ma con - so - la, e giu - bi - lar mi

pride, can sa - tis - fy, can sa - tis - fy my pride! I'll........ show him I'm his
fa, e giu-bi - lar, e giu - bi - lar mi fa! Ah, che la-sciar-ti in

mas - ter, No more shall he de - fy me. Dare he be so pre -
pa - ce non vo' que-sto con - ten - to, tu non na - sce - sti, au -

sumptuous As ven - ture thus to thwart me? Dare he, my ser-vant,
-da-ce, per da - re a me tor - men-to, e for-se an-cor per

laugh at me, yes laugh at me, While I.......... am mor - ti -fied?
ri - de-re, per ri - de-re di mia.....in-fe - li - ci - tà.

I will en-dure no long-er, Ven-geance a-lone in - spires me, 'Tis
Già la spe-ran-za so - la del - le ven-det - te mi - e, quest'

ven - geance, on - ly ven-geance Can sa - tis-fy my pride, can sa-tis-
a - ni-ma con - so-la, e giu - bi-lar mi fa, e.... giu-bi-

-fy, can sa - tis-fy, can sa-tis-fy my pride,..............
-lar, e giu - bi-lar mi fa, e... giu-bi - lar,..............

Recitative

Enter Marcellina, Don Curzio, Figaro and Bartolo

Curzio (stammering)

I have giv'n my de-ci-sion: he must mar-ry her or pay her. That's what the
È de-ci-sa la li-te, o pa-gar-la, o spo-sar-la, o-ra am-mu-

court says. Now I'm hap-py. I am wretch-ed! At last the man I
-ti-te. Io re-spi-ro. Ed io mo-ro. (Al-fin spo-sa io sa-

Figaro
Cur. crowns, sir? I am a no-ble-man, and I can-not mar-ry with-out the con-sent of my
du - ri. Son gen-til-uo - mo, e sen - za l'as-sen - so de' miei no-bi-li pa

Count **Figaro**
F. par - ents. And where are they? who are they? I wish some-one would
-ren - ti— Do - ve so - no? chi so - no? Lac - scia-te an - cor cer -

Bartolo
F. find them; for the last ten years I have hop'd to come a-cross them. Found on the
-car - li; do - po die - ci an - ni io spe - ro di tro-var - li. Qual - che bam

Figaro **Count**
B. door-step, were you? No, but lost there, I think, or ra-ther sto - len. Sto - len?
-bin tro - va - to? Nò per - du - to, dot - tor, an - zi ru - ba - to. Co - me!

Marcellina **Bartolo** **Curzio** **Figaro**
Sto - len? Your proof, sir! Can you bring wit - nes-ses? Proofs? yes, in-deed, sir! the
Co - sa? La pro - va? Il te - sti - mo - nio? L'o - ro, le gem - me, ei

F. fine em-broid-er'd cloth-ing, yes, and the je - wels and gold too found on me by the
ri - ca - ma - ti pan - ni, che ne' più te - ne - ri an - ni mi ri-tro-va-ron a

rob-bers when they stole me,— what bet-ter proof is want-ed of my birth and my
-dos-so i ma-sna-die-ri, so-no gl'in-di-zü ve-ri di mia na-sci-ta il-

breeding? And, in ad-di-tion, here on my arm a ve-ry curious birth-mark— What? a
-lu-stre: e so-pra tut-to que-sto al mio brac-cio im-pres-so ge-ro-gli-fi-co— U-na

Figaro **Marcellina**

straw-ber-ry mark u-pon your right arm? And how did you know? Oh, hea-vens! 'tis
spa-to-la im-pres-so al brac-cio de-stro? E a voi ch'il dis-se? Oh Di-o! è

Curzio Count Bartolo Marcellina **Bartolo**

he then, 'Tis I in-deed, ma'am. Who? Who? Who? Ra-fa-el-lo! By robbers you were
des-so! E ver, son i-o, Chi? Chi? Chi? Ra-fa-el-lo! E i la-dri ti ra-

Figaro **Bartolo** **Figaro** **Bartolo**

stol'n? Yes, near a cas-tle. Be-hold your mo-ther! My nurse, sir? No, your
-pir? Pres-so un ca-stel-lo. Ec-co tua ma-dre. Ba-li-a? No; tua

Curzio and Count **Figaro** **Marcellina (impressively)**

mo-ther. His mo-ther! What can this mean? There stands your fa-ther!
ma-dre. Sua ma-dre? Co-sa sen-to! Ec-co tuo pa-dre.

The Marriage of Figaro

B. & H. 15960

Nº 18 Sextet

*Allegro moderato

* The tempo indication of the Sextet is Andante in Mozart's manuscript.
The Marriage of Figaro

B. & H. 159

The Marriage of Figaro

228

The Marriage of Figaro

B.& H. 159

Susanna

230

The Marriage of Figaro

B. & H. 15960

The Marriage of Figaro

The Marriage of Figaro

The Marriage of Figaro

B.& H. 15960

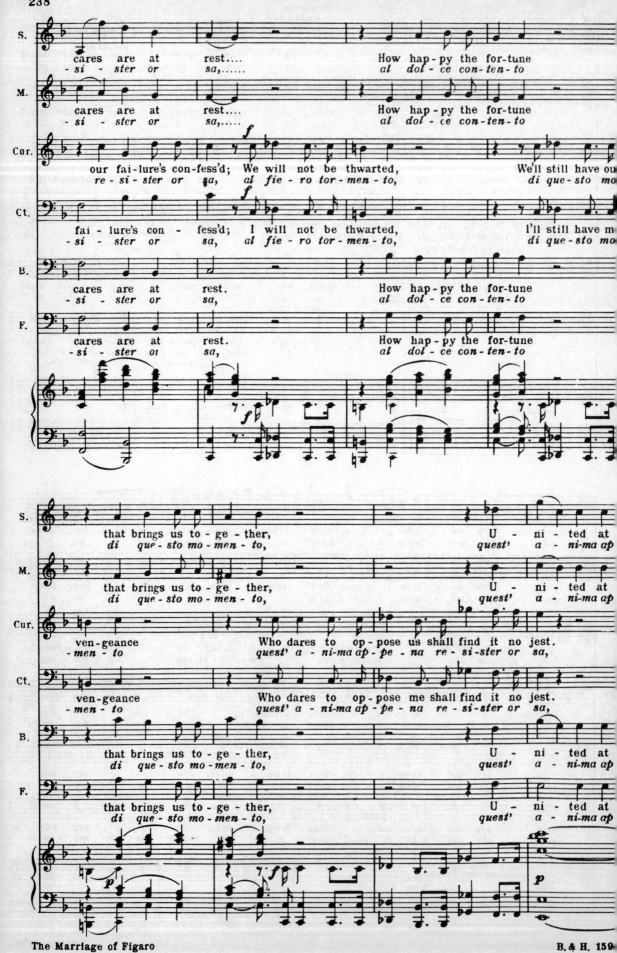

The Marriage of Figaro

B.& H. 15960

Exit Count and Don Curzio

Recitative

Marcellina

To think that we have found him, the lit-tle darling that we used to be so fond of!
Ec-co-vi, o ca - ro a - mi - co, il dol-ce frut-to dell' an - ti - co amor no-stro.

Bartolo
That lit-tle
Or non par

e-pi-sode I thought was dead and bu-ried. Well, as we've found him, I'll ad-mit that he's my son.
-lia-mo di fat-ti si ri-mo-ti; e-gli è mio fi-glio, mia con-sor-te voi sie-te,

I sup-pose I shall have to mar-ry you now.
e le noz-ze fa-rem quan-do vo-le-te.

Marcellina
Yes, do! and this ve-ry
Og-gi; e dop-pie sa-

(to Figaro)
day too! Take this; here is the con-tract, for the mo-ney you
-ran-no, pren-di, que-sto il bi-gliet-to del de-nar che a me

(giving paper)
owe me, as a wedding present.
de-vi, ed è tua do-te.

Susanna (giving purse)
And the mo-ney to pay it.
Pren-di an-cor que-sta bor-sa.

Bartolo (another purse)
And this from me too!
E que-sta an-co-ra.

Figaro
Thank you! I'll take as much as you like to give me.
Bra-vi! git-ta-te pur, ch'io pi-glio o-gno-ra.

Susanna
Now we must go and tell all our good
Vo-lia-mo ad in-for-mar d'ogni av-ven-

for-tune to my la-dy and my un-cle. Could a-ny one be
-tu-ra Ma-da-mae no-stro Zi-o. Chi al par di me con-

hap-pier in all the world than I am? I am! I am!
-ten-tal Chi al par di me con-ten-tal I - o! I - o!

Marcellina Susanna Marcellina cresc. All exeunt laughing
I am! And if my lord is fu-rious, so much the bet-ter!
I - o! E schiat-ti il si-gnor Con-te al gu-sto mi - o!

Bartolo Figaro

Enter Barbarina and Cherubino
Barbarina
Now, come with me, Che-ru-bi-no; we'll go to our house. Who do you
An-diam, an-diam, bel pag-gio, in ca-sa mi-a tut-te ri-

think you'll find there? All the pret-ti-est girls there are in the vil-lage; but
-tro-ve-ra-i le più bel-le ra-gaz-ze del ca-stel-lo, di

Nº 19 Recitative and Aria

Enter Countess
Countess

Andante

Is Su-san-na not here?
E Su-san-na non vien!

I'm im-pa-tient to be
so-no an-sio-sa di sa-

told what his lordship has said to her pro-po-sal.
-per co-me il con-te ac-col-se la pro-po-sta,

And yet I'm doubtful if it
Al-quan-to ar-di-to il pro-

Allegretto

was not too bold;
-get-to mi par,

my lord is al-ways so im-pul-sive and so jea-lous.
ad u-no spo-so sì vi-va-ce e ge-lo-so!

Andante

But what's the harm?
Ma che mal c'è?

I keep the as-sig-
can-gian-do-i miei ve-

-nation wear-ing Su-san-na's dress, while she wears mine.
-sti-ti con quel-li di Su-san-na, ei suoi co' mie-i

B. & H. 15960

Recitative

Enter Count and Antonio

Antonio

I can tell you my lord, that Che-ru-bi-no has not yet left the
Io vi di-co si-gnor, che Che-ru-bi-no è an-co-ra nel ca-

cas-tle, here's his hat for a proof of what I'm say-ing,
-stel-lo, e ve-de-te per pro-va il suo cap-pel-lo.

Count

But how can he be
Ma co-me se a quest'

here still? Why, he ought by this time to be at Sev-ille.
o-ra es-ser giun-to a Si-vi-glia e-gli do-vri-a?

Antonio

It seems, my lord, that to-
Scu-sa-te, og-gi Si-

-day Seville's at my house. He's been dress'd as a girl there, and
-vi-glia è a ca-sa mi-a. Là ve-stis-si da don-na, e

there it is that he's left his o-ther clothes. Where's the boy?
là la-scia-ti ha gl'al-tri a-bi-ti suoi. Per-fi-dil

Count **Antonio**

My lord,
An-diam

Exit Count and Antonio

come with me and I'll show you.
e li ve-dre-te vo-i.

B. & H. 15960

Countess
Well, did you tell him? What was his lordship's ans-wer?
Co - sa mi nar - ri? e che ne dis-se il Con - te?

Susanna
Oh, there was no mis-
Gli si leg-ge-va in

S.
-tak-ing that my lord's ve - ry ang-ry.
fron-te il di-spet-to e la rab-bia.

Countess
Well done! It will be
Pia - no, che me-glio

Cts.
eas-i-er now to catch him. And where did you in-vite him to
or lo por-re-mo in gab-bia! dov' è l'ap-pun-ta-men-to, che

Cts.
look for you this ev-'ning?
tu gli pro-po-ne-sti?

Susanna
In the gar-den.
In giar-di-no.

Countess
We'll make it clear-er.
Fis-siam-gli un lo-co.

Susanna
Write to him. I write to him? oh, my la-dy!
Scri - vi. Ch'io scri-va, ma si-gno-ra—

Countess
Write what I
Eh scri-vi,

Cts.
tell you, I take the whole re-spon-si-bi-li-ty.
di-co, e tut-to io pren-do su me stes-sa;

Have you ev-'ry-thing ready?
Can-zo-net-ta sull' a-ria—

B. & H. 15960

Nº 20 Duet Susanna and Countess

Recitative

№ 21 Chorus

Enter Barbarina with peasant girls, and Cherubino dressed as a peasant girl. All carry bunches of flowers.

Grazioso

Sopranos I and II

No - ble la - dy, here we
Ri - ce - ve - te, o pa - dron-

of - fer fair - est flow'rs that we can find, They were pluck'd at ear - ly mor - ning Ere the
- ci - na, que - ste ro - se e que - sti fior, che ab-biam col - ti sta-mat - ti - na, per mo-

sun on them had shined.
strar-vi-il no-stro a-mor.

Sim-ple flow'rs are all.... we
Sia-mo tan - te con - ta -

bring you, sim-ple songs are all...we sing you, of de - vo - tion, love and
- di - ne, e siam tut - te po - ve - ri - ne, Ma quel po - co che re -

Recitative

Barbarina

If it please your la-dy-ship, we are girls from the vil-lage; we hope that
Que-ste so-no, Ma-da-ma, le ra-gaz-ze del lo-co che il po-co

you will not re-fuse these flow-ers— they are all we can give you, beg-ging your
ch'han vi ven-go-no ad of-fri-re, e vi chie-don per-don del lo-ro ar-

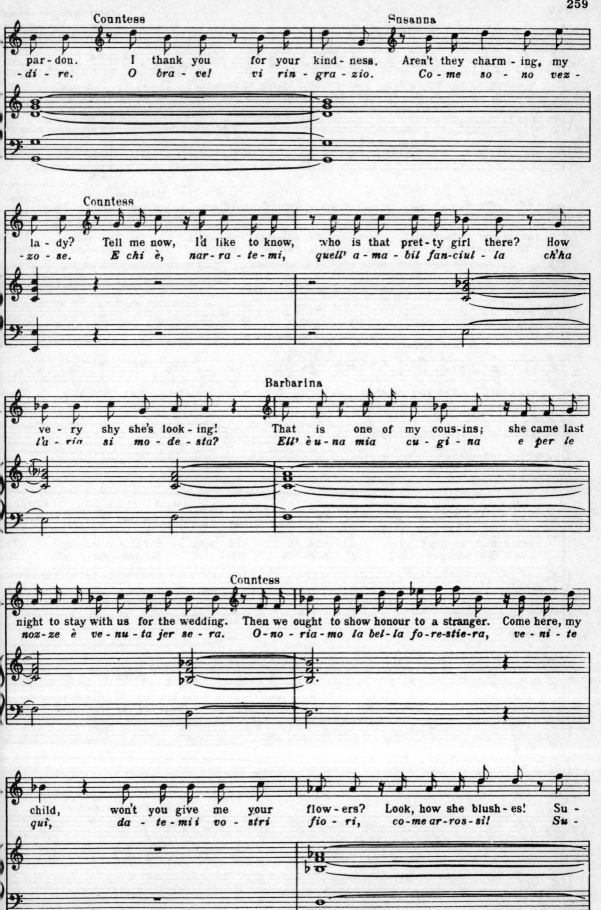

The Marriage of Figaro

Enter the Count and Ant▨
behind. Antonio pulls▨
Cherubino's head-dress▨
puts on his soldier's hat▨

Cts. -san-na, do you not no-tice a re-sem-blance to someone? The ve-ry im-age!
-san-na, e non ti pa-re— che so - mi-gli ad al - cu - no. Al na-tu - ra-le.

Antonio. Countess. Susanna.
Caught you at last, sir! Here is the gal-lant cap-tain! Oh, hea-vens! Lit-tl
Eh co-spet-ta-te! è que-sti l'uf-fi - zia - te! Oh stel-le! Ma-la

Count. Countess.
S. ras-cal! Can you ex-plain this? I must in-form your lord-ship, I'm s
-dri-no! Eb-ben Ma-da-ma— Io so - no,o si-gnor mi - o, ir-r

Count Countes
Cts. pris'd and an-noy'd too, no less than you are. But this morn-ing? Thi
-ta - ta e sor-pre-sa al par di vo - i. Ma sta-ma - ne? Ste

Cts. morn-ing, I ad-mit we in-tend-ed to dress him up in girl's clothes, as yo
-ma - ne, per l'o-dier - na fe - sta vo - le-vam tra-ve-stir-lo al mo - de

Count (to Cherubino)
Cts. see him, to make some fun this ev-'ning. What are you do-ing
stes - so che l'han ve-sti-to a - des - so. E per-chè non par

B. & H. 15

A. girl! You're pret-ty sharp at pick-ing up your les-sons. Is it a plot, of
-gliuo-la! hai buon ma-e-stro, che ti fa la sco-la. (Non so,qual uom, qual

Count (aside)

Ct. man, woman, or de-vil that puts me in the wrong at ev'ry mo-ment?
de-mo-ne, qual di-o, ri-vol-ga tut-to quan-to a tor-to mi-o.)

Enter Figaro

Figaro
My lord, if you keep all these girls here waiting for nothing, we shall not have a-ny
Si-gnor, se trat-te-ne-te tut-te que-ste ra gaz-ze, ad-dio fe-ste, ad-dio

F. danc-ing. In - deed? with your in-jur'd foot you think of
dan-za. E che? vor-re-sti bal-lar col piè stra-

Count

Figaro
Ct. danc-ing? I do not feel it much now. Come, girls, the mu-sic's
-vol-to? Eh non mi duol più mol-to, an-diam, bel-le fan-

F. wait-ing! How will he ev-er manage to es-cape now? Oh, you may safe-ly
-ciul-le. (Co-me si ca-ve-rà dall'im-ba-raz-zo.) (La-scia-te fa-re a

Countess (to Susanna)   Susanna (to Countess)

264

The Marriage of Figaro

B. & H. 15960

N.º 22 Finale

now; Besides, there's one bride who's in your special favour.   Be seat-ed.
-biam;   al-fin si trat-ta d'u-na vo-stra pro-tet-ta.   Seg-gia-mo!

(aside)

The Count and Countess sit down on two thron

will, ma'am,   and plan revenge up-on them.
-gia-mol   e me-di-tiam ven-det-ta.

un poco cresc.

Enter the wedding procession: two you

girls bearing Susanna's bridal hat and veil. Antonio leads Susanna to the Count; she kneels and receives the ve

etc., from him. Figaro leads Marcellina to the Countess; similar business. The two wedding couples sit on stool

facing the thrones during the singing of the song by two young girls.

B. & H. 1596

Allegretto

2 Young Girls

Come all faith-ful lov - ers and
A man - ti co - stan - ti se -

join us in song, To him.... who re - leased us From shame and from
-gua - ci d'o - nor, can - ta - te, lo - da - te, si sag - gio si-

Susanna, while kneeling before the Count, gives him the letter

which he hides

FANDANGO

Andante

The Count reads the letter and pricks his finger with the pin.

B. & H. 1596

B.& H. 15960

272

F. fin-ger.
di - to,

Now you see he has dropp'd the pin and can-not
il Nar-ci-so or la cer-ca, oh che stor-

F. find it.
-di -tol

Recit
Count
Good friends and neighbours, we'll
An - da - te a - mi - ci! e

Maestoso

Ct. ce - le - brate this ev-'ning the marriage of these two hap - py cou - ples in a
sia per que-sta se - ra di - spo-sto l'ap - pa - ra - to nu-zia - le col - la

Ct. right mer - ry fash - ion. It is my wish that the night should pass in feast-ing; we'll have
più ric - ca pom-pa! io vo' che si - a ma-gni - fi - ca la fe - sta, e

The Marriage of Figaro

B. & H. 15960

The Marriage of Figaro

End of Act III

B. & H. 15960

ACT IV

A garden, arbours right and left

№ 23 Cavatina

Andante

Barbarina enters with a lantern looking for something on the ground.

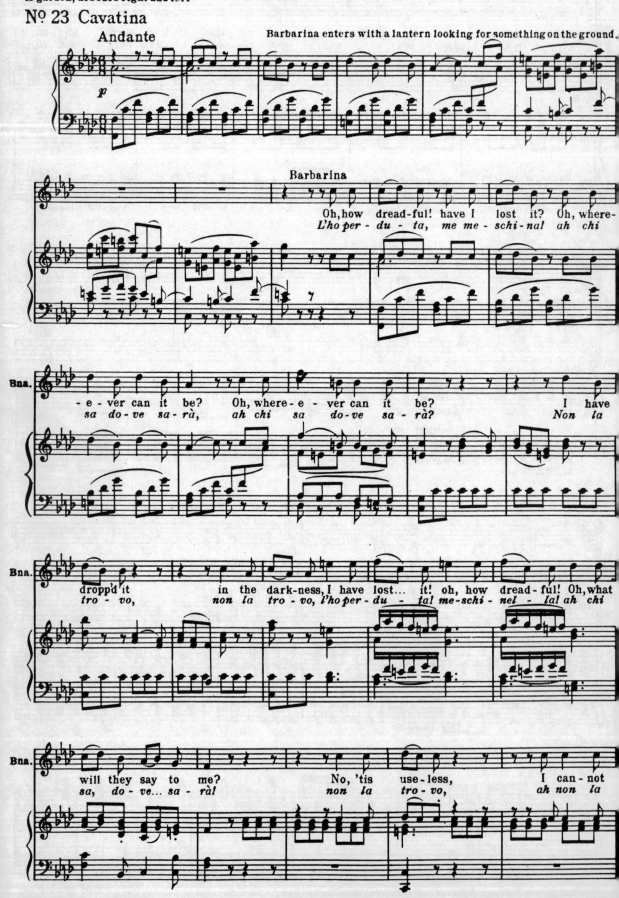

Barbarina

Oh, how dread-ful! have I lost it? Oh, where-
L'ho per - du - ta, me me - schi-na! ah chi

- e - ver can it be? Oh, where-e - ver can it be? I have
sa do - ve sa - rà, ah chi sa do - ve sa - rà? Non la

dropp'd it in the dark-ness, I have lost... it! oh, how dread-ful! Oh, what
tro - vo, non la tro - vo, l'ho per - du - ta! me-schi - nel - la! ah chi

will they say to me? No, 'tis use-less, I can-not
sa, do - ve... sa - rà! non la tro - vo, ah non la

Recitative

Enter Marcellina and Figaro.

*if Recitative follows, the last bar coincides with its 1st bar.

The Marriage of Figaro

B. & H. 15960

The Marriage of Figaro

B.& H.15960

282

Nº 24 Aria

Tempo di Menuetto

Marcellina

Through-out the realm of na-ture, when spring-time bids them
Il ca-pro e la ca-pret-ta, son sem-pre in a-mi-

M. pair,... We see how ev'ry happy crea-ture Its joy........ in... peace can share. The
-stà,..... l'a-gnel-lo all' a-gnel-let-ta, la guer-ra mai non fa...... Le

M. wild est and most cru-el, Through path less for-est rang-ing
più fe-ro-ci bel-ve, per sel-ve e per cam-pagn

M. Shows to his mate, un-changing, His love and ten-der care. Shows to his mate, un-
la-scian le lor com-pa-gne in pa-ce e li-ber-tà,... la-scian le lor com-

B. & H. 15960

Recitative

Enter Barbarina

Barbarina

The ar-bour on the left hand, I think he told me; is this it? yes,
Nel pa-di-glio-ne a man-ca, ei co-sì dis-se, è que-sto, è

that's right. I hope he won't for-get me. These peo-ple are so
que-sto. E poi se non ve-nis-se? ah ah! che bra-va

naugh-ty! I hard-ly got them to give me an o-range or a
gen-te! a sten-to dar-mi un a-ran-cio, u-na pe-ra, e u-na ciam-

bis-cuit. 'And who's to eat this sup-per?' 'It's for a friend of
-bel-la. "Per chi, ma-da-mi-gel-la?" "Oh per qual-cun, si-

mine, sir.' 'I thought as much!' Well, well!
-gno-re." "Già lo sap-piam," eb-be-ne!

The Marriage of Figaro

B. & H. 15960

The Marriage of Figaro

You are in-vit-ed here to wit-ness the an-cient pri-vi-lege of the lord of the
in que-sto stes-so lo - co ce - le - bre - rem la fe - sta del - la mia spo-sa o-

Man - or, grant-ed by my vir-tuous wife. Oh, shall we real - ly? I
- ne - sta e del feu-dal si - gnor. (Ah buo - no, buo - no, ca -

Basilio

see now how it stands: They've ar-rang'd it with-out em-ploy-ing me.
- pi - sco co-me e-gli è, ac - cor - da - ti si son sen-za di me.)

Figaro

You will stay here and wait where no one can see you. I have to go and make fur-ther ar-
Voi da que-sti con-tor - ni non vi sco-sta - te, in-tan-to io va - do a dar cer -

- range-ments; I'll come back in a mo-ment. Then, when I whis - tle, you'll
- ti or - di - ni, e tor-no in po-chi i-stan - ti. A un fi-schio mi - o cor -

F. all rush out to-geth-er.
-re - te tut - ti quan - ti.

Exit **Basilio**
The man's possess'd by de-vils!
(Ha i dia - vo - li nel cor - po.)

Bartolo
What has de-
Ma co - sa,

Basilio
B. -rang'd him? No-thing. His lord-ship likes Su-san-na; she has giv'n him to-night an as-sig-
quan - ti? Nul - la. Su - san - na pia-ce al Con-te, el-la d'ac-cor-do gli diè un ap-pun-ta-

Bartolo
Bas. -na-tion, which Fi-ga-ro does not like. Bless my soul! You think he ought not to re-
-men - to ch'a Fi-ga-ro non pia - ce. E che? dun-que do-vria sof-frir-lo in

Basilio
B. -sent it? Ma-ny a man has en - dur'd it; why should he make ob-
pa - ce. Quel-che sof - fro-no tan - ti, ei sof-frir non po-

Bas. -jec - tions? And then, con - si - der; if he did, where's the gain? You know the
-treb - be? e poi sen - ti - te che gua - da - gno può far? nel mon-do, a-

fa - ble, how the pot and the ket - tle went a jour-ney to-geth - er; need I

-mi - co, l'ac-coz-zar - la con gran - di, fu pe - ri - co - lo o-gno - ra, dan no-

tell you in this case which will get bro - ken?

-van - ta per cen - to e han vin - to an - co - ra.

№ 25 Aria

Andante   Basilio

Youth will

In quegl'-

not give heed to rea-son, As my own sad past could show; For both

an-ni, in cui val po - co la mal pra - ti-ca ra - gion, ebbi anch'

in and out of sea - son I did fool-ish things, I know. Ah! but

io lo stes - so fo - co, fui quel paz-zo, ch'or non son, fui quel

Bas.

I seiz'd the ass's skin, wrapp'd it well round me, For I had nothing else
Ec - co - le mem - bra co - prir mi gio - va col man - to d'a - si - no,

Bas.

to keep me dry, for I had nothing else to keep me dry. The storm w
che mi do - nò, col man - to d'a - si - no che mi do - nò. Fi - ni - sce il

Bas.

o - ver soon, and off I start-ed, When some fe-roc-ious beast straight at... me
tur - bi - ne, io fo due pas-si. Che fie - ra or-ri - bi - le dian - zi a me..

Bas.

dart - ed; Its eyes were gleam-ing, its chops wer
fas - si; già, già mi toc - ca, l'in - gor - da

Bas.

steam-ing, And to... de-fend my-self how could I try?
boc - ca, già di... di - fen - der - mi spe - me non ho,

B. & H. 1596

Nº 26 Recitative and Aria

RECIT.

Enter Figaro

Ev-'ry-thing's rea-dy; it must be time for their ap-point-ment. Did I hear
Tut-to è di-spo-sto; l'o-ra do-vreb-be es-ser vi-ci-na; io sen-to

foot-steps? Su-san-na? Not a soul! I can see nothing.
gen-te— è des-sa! non è al-cun; bu-ja è la not-te,

Andante

So I be-gin this ev-'ning to learn the wretch-ed trade that it is to be a
ed io co-min-cio o-ma-i a fa-re il sci-mu-ni-to me-stie-re di ma-

hus-band. The trait-ress! To de-ceive me at the
-ri-to. In-gra-ta! Nel mo-men-to del-la

ve-ry last mo-ment! I saw him read her let-ter, I saw him laugh too, laugh'd my-
mia ce-ri-mo-nia ei go-de-va leg-gen-do; e nel ve-der-lo, io ri-

F. -self, lit-tle know-ing what I laugh'd at. Oh, Su-san-na, Su-
-de - va di me sen-za sa-per - lo. O Su-san-na! Su-

F. -san - na! Have you brought me to this then? Those
-san - na! quan - ta pe - na mi co - sti! con

F. eyes so sweet and can-did, and that face so in-ge-nuous,
quell' in - ge - nua fac - cia, con que-gli oc-chi inno - cen - ti,

F. who would not have be-liev'd them? What's he who trusts a
chi cre - du - to l'a - vri - a? ah! che il fi - dar - sia

F. wo-man, a wo-man? Fool, fool and fool a-gain!
don - na, a don - na, è o - gnor fol - li - a.

B. & H. 15960

B. & H. 15966

leave you. For coaxing and cry-ing ca-jol-ing and cheating, in-triguing and lying, they cannot be
-li-gne, ma-e-stre d'in-gan-ni, a-mi-che d'af-fan-ni, che fin-go-no, men-to-no, a-mo-re non

bea-ten. No mer-cy they show, no mer-cy they show, no, no, no,
sen-ton, non sen-ton pie-tà, non sen-ton pie-tà, no, no, no,

cresc.

no! The rest we'll pass o-ver in si-lence, What happens you all of you know.
no. Il re-sto, il re-sto nol di-co, già o-gnu-no, già ognu-no lo sa.

p

sf p

Yes, fools you are, and will be, Fools, till your eyes are
A-pri-te un po' que-gli oc-chi, uo-mi-ni in-cau-tie

cresc.

fp

o-pen'd, Un-til you learn what wo-men are, And know them through and
scioc-chi, guar-da-te que-ste fem-mi-ne, guar-da-te co-sa

The Marriage of Figaro

Recitative

Enter the Countess and Susanna, disguised in each other's dresses. Afterwards enter Marcellina.

Susanna

My la-dy, here's Mar-cel-li-na says Fi-ga-ro is com-ing. He's here al-
Si - gno-ra! el - la mi dis-se che Fi-ga-ro ver-rav-vi. An - zi è ve-

Marcellina

M. -rea-dy, so speak a lit-tle low-er.
-nu - to, ab-bas-sa un po' la vo - ce.

Susanna

One lo-ver list-'ning, the
Dun-que un ci à-scol-ta, e

S. o-ther on the point of ar-riv-ing! We can be-gin.
l'al - tro dee ve - nir a cer-car-mi, in-co-min-ciam!

Marcellina

I'll hide with-in this
Io vo-gliò quì ce-

(Enters arbour on left)

M. ar-bour.
-lar - mi.

Susanna (to Countess)

But ma-dam, you are trem-bling; you feel it cold here?
Ma - da - ma voi tre - ma - te, a - vre-ste fred-do?

Countess

The
Par-

Cts. night is ra-ther chil-ly; I shall go in now.
-miu-mi-da la not-te; io mi ri-ti-ro.

Figaro

Now we shall see the
(Ec - co - ci del - la

B. & H. 15960

F.
great dra - ma - tic mo - ment. I should pre - fer to stay here, if your
cri - si al gran - de i - stan - te.) Io sot - to que - ste pian - te, (se ma -

S.
la - dy-ship will al - low me, and take the air a lit - tle a - mong the
-da - ma il per - met - te,) re - sto al pren - de - re il fre - sco u - na mezz'

S. *Figaro* *Countess*
pine - trees. To take the air— a - mong the pine - trees! Yes, by all means
o - ra. Il fre - sco! il fre - sco! Re - sta - ci in buon'

Cts. *Susanna*
do so. That ras - cal Fi - ga - ro's watch - ing, he shall have his re -
o - ra. (Il bir - bo è in sen - ti - nel - la, di - ver - tiam - ci an - che

S.
- ward too. I'll pay him out for dar - ing to sus - pect me.
no - i, dia - mo - gli la mer - cè de' dub - bi suo - i.)

Nº 27 Recitative and Aria

Allegro vivace assai

RECIT

Susanna

Now at last comes the moment when I yield, un-re-sist-ing,   to   joy in his em-bra-ces.
Giun-se al-fin il mo-men-to, che go-drò sen-za affan-no   in   brac-cio all'i-dol mi - o.

Susanna

Why need I trem-ble?   A - way with sil - ly scruples! shall they stand in the way of my   de-
Ti - mi - de cu - rel   u - sci - te dal mio pet-to,   a tur - bar non ve - ni-te il mio di-

S.

sires?   Here   is   this   wood—'twas made for lo-vers'
-let-to!   *Oh   co - me   par che all' a - mo - ro - so*

ARIA
Andante

Susanna

The Marriage of Figaro

The Marriage of Figaro

Recitative

Figaro

How shameless! Then all a-long she meant to de - ceive me! Am I a-wake or
Per - fi - da! e in quel-la for - ma me - co men - ti - a; non so s'io ve-glio o

dream - ing? La, la, la, la, la, la, la, le - ra. That's Che - ru - bi - no! I heard a
dor - mo. La, la, la, la, la, la, la, le - ra. Il pic-ciol pag-gio. Io sen - to

Cherubino (enters singing)   **Countess**   **Cherubino**

voice then; I must try to find Bar - ba - ri - na. Ah, there I see a
gen - te, en - tri - a-mo o-ve en-trò Bar - ba - ri - na, oh, ve - do qui u - na

Countess   **Cherubino**

pet-ti-coat. What shall I do now? That must be - no, I was wrong there — by the
don - na. Ahi - me me-schi - na! M'in - gan - no! a quel cap-pel - lo che nell'

Countess

head-dress I know it is Su - san - na. If my Lord finds me now, then all is o - ver!
om-bra vegg' io, par-mi Su-san - na. E se il Con-te o - ra vien, sor - te ti-ran-na!

                    B. & H. 15960

№ 28 Finale

Countess

B. & H. 15960

314

The Marriage of Figaro

B. & H. 15960

B. & H. 15960

316

The Marriage of Figaro

B. & H. 15960

The Marriage of Figaro

B.& H. 15980

B. & H. 15960

320

The Marriage of Figaro

B. & H. 15980

Con un poco più di moto

Figaro and Susanna retire to opposite corners of the stage.

The Marriage of Figaro

The Marriage of Figaro

Susanna
A les-son 'tis for hus-bands, yes, for hus-bands, Who
Ma-ri-ti sci-mu-ni-ti, sci-mu-ni-ti, ve-
Ct.
here. Then Ve-nus now must hide her light;
-lar! en-triam, mia bel-la Ve-ne-re,
Figaro
A les-son 'tis for hus-bands, Who think........
Ma-ri-ti sci-mu-ni-ti, ve-ni-
sf p sf p
S.
think they've naught to fear, no, naught to fear.
-ni-te ad im-pa-rar, ad im-pa-rar.
Countess
I think it's rather dark there.
Al bu-jo, si-gnor mi-o?
Ct.
They must not find us here.
an-dia-mo-ci a ce-lar!
The dark-er 'tis, the
È quel-lo che vogl'
F.
.... they've naught to fear.
- te ad im-pa-rar!
Ct.
bet-ter. I don't sup-pose that you will need a can-dle there, my
i-o, tu sai che là per leg-ge-re io non de-sio d'en-
sf p

B. & H. 15960

B. & H. 15960

The Marriage of Figaro

B. & H. 15960

The Marriage of Figaro

S. ......phil-an - - der-ing, and that's what you will get, yes
-ra o per - - fi-do! a fa-re il se-dut-tor, a

F. sign,......... as... sign of love, and suf-fer no re-gret, and
gra - zio-sis-si-mil o mio fe-li-ce a-mor, o

S. that's what you will get, yes, that's what you will get.
fa-re il se-dut - tor, a fa-re il se-dut - tor.

F. suf - fer no re - gret,.... no, no re - gret.
mio fe - li-ce a - mor,..... fe - li - ce a - mor.

F. Now Su - san-na, be kind and for-give me; All in vain did you try to de-
Pa - ce, pa-ce, mio dol - ce te-so-rol io co-nob-bi la vo-ce che a-

Andante

Susanna (surprised and laughing)

Then you knew me?
La mia vo - ce?

F. - ceive me; Why, your voice told me plain-ly 'twas you. You
- do - ro, e che im-pres-sa o-gnor ser - bo nel cor. La

The Marriage of Figaro

B. & H. 15960

The Marriage of Figaro

They go towards the
left hand arbour.

S.

up for the pains of the past, to......make up for the pains of the past.
pe - ne com-pen-si il pia - cer, e........ le pe - ne com-pen-si il pia - cer.

F.

up for the pains of the past, to......make up for the pains of the past.
pe - ne com-pen-si il pia - cer, e........ le pe - ne com-pen-si il pia - cer.

Count (seizing Figaro)

Ho, you men, there, Ho bring lights here! (pretending to be terrified) Help me, help me, come this
Gen - te, gen-tel all'ar-mi, all' ar - mi! Gen - te, gen-tel a-ju - tol a-

F.

'Tis his lord-ship!
Il pa - dro - ne!

Allegro assai

Enter Basilio, Curzio, Bartolo and Antonio
Basilio and Curzio

What has happen'd, what has happen'd?
Cos' av-ven - ne? cos' av-ven - ne?

Ct.

way now!
- ju - tol

Bartolo and Antonio

What has happen'd, what has happen'd?
Cos' av-ven - ne? cos' av-ven - ne?

F.

I am ru - in'd!
Son per - du - to!

Ct.

See, here's a vil-lain has in - sul - ted and be - tray'd me, and with
Il scel - le - ra - to m'ha tra - di - to, m'ha in-fa - ma - to, e con

 B. & H. 15960

The Count goes to the arbour and hands out successively Cherubino, Barbarina, Marcellina and Susanna

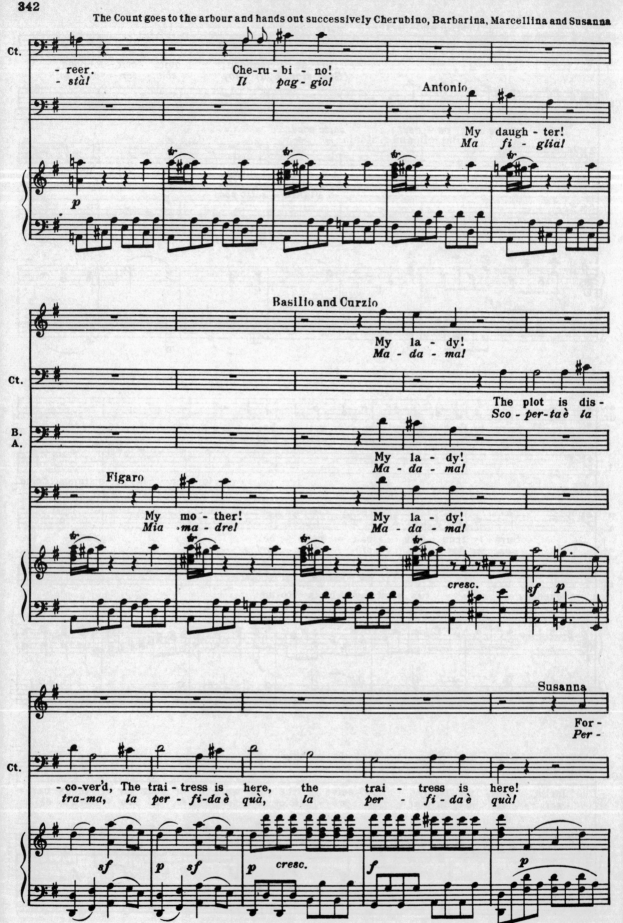

The Countess comes out of the right-hand arbour

B. & H. 15960

B. & H. 15960

The Marriage of Figaro

The Marriage of Figaro

B. & H. 15960

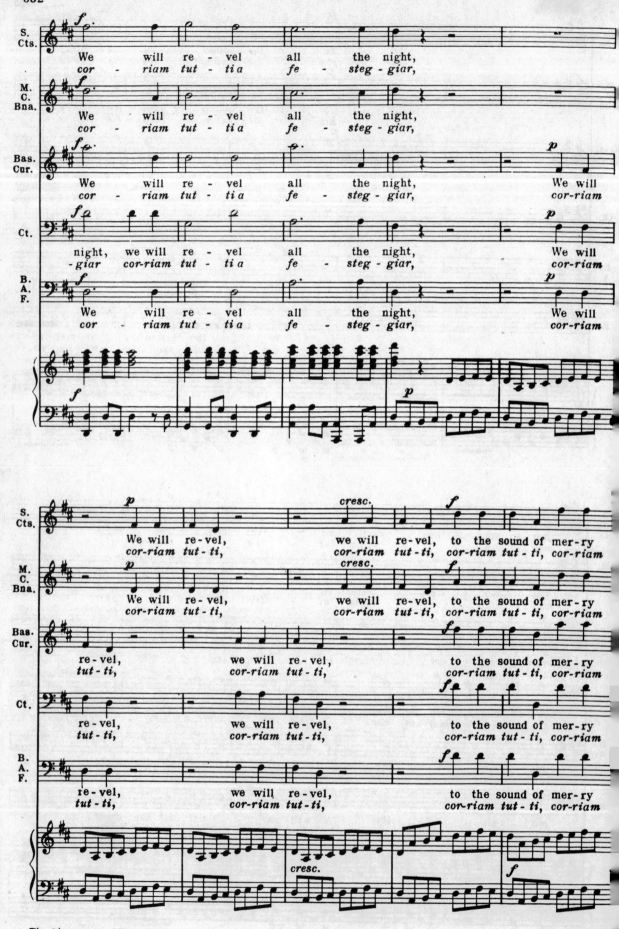

The Marriage of Figaro